A HISTORY OF
ENGINEERING
DRAWING

BY

Peter Jeffrey Booker

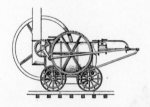

1963

CHATTO & WINDUS

LONDON

Published by
Chatto and Windus Ltd
42 William IV Street
London W.C.2
*
Clarke, Irwin and Co Ltd
Toronto

Printed in Great Britain by
R. and R. Clark Ltd
Edinburgh

A HISTORY OF ENGINEERING DRAWING

To Draughtsmen
past, present and future

'The charm which accompanies these studies will conquer the repugnance which men have in general for intense thought, and make them find pleasure in that exercise of their intellect which almost all regard as painful and irksome.'

Gaspard Monge, 1795

'These things are extremely plain and agreeable to persons of clear heads and of a genius turned to painting, let them be couched in terms ever so rude; but to men of low capacities and of minds not formed for these politer arts, though explained by the most eloquent pens, they would still be unpleasant.'

Leone Battista Alberti, 1435

Contents

List of Plates

Acknowledgements

Acknowledgement is made to the following institutions, authors, and publishers for permission to reproduce illustrations and quotations:

Trustees of the British Museum for Plates 1 and 2 and Figs. 9, 13, 14, 23 (a and b), 24, 29, 31, 32, 37, 38, 39, 45, 52 (part), 56 and 88; Director, the Science Museum, London, for Plate 3; Librarian, Pepysian Library, Magdalene College, Cambridge, for Plates 4, 5 and 7; Keeper, Museum of Science and Industry, Birmingham, for Plate 6; Dominion Engineering Company Ltd., and the late Mr. George Noble for Plate 8, and Figs. 74 and 76; U.S. Patent Office and Eastman Kodak Company Ltd., Rochester, N.Y., U.S.A., for Fig. 63; General Dynamics/Electronics, San Diego, U.S.A., for Figs. 92, 93 and 94; Longmans, Green & Co., Ltd., and Mr. E. D. Low for quotations from *An Introduction to Machine Drawing and Design*; Comptroller, Her Majesty's Stationery Office, for quotations from *Dimensional Analysis of Engineering Designs*; Ferranti, Ltd., Edinburgh, for Fig. 91; British Standards Institution for quotations from B.S. 308 and for illustrations based on those in this standard. (The current standard is available from B.S.I., 2 Park Street, London, W.1, and a cheaper abridged version is published for students.)

Preface

THE pencil has been called the most potent instrument in the world, for it gives most of man's thoughts and aspirations their first visible form.

Drawings are like windows through which we see things. The draughtsman, who is a maker of these windows, appreciates the effort put into them much more so than others, who only see *through* drawings, as it were, to the things themselves depicted and so take drawing for granted.

In its narrowest sense engineering drawing is a language used for communication. However, languages in general are not only useful for communication; they play an inherent part in our very thinking, for we tend to think in terms of the languages we know. Drawing is of this nature, and he who can draw can think of, and deal with, many things and problems which another man cannot. Between thinking and communication, in the form of geometry, drawing has another function; it allows us to predetermine the shapes we require and it is, therefore, a primary tool of design.

Engineering drawing is not, however, the same as engineering design; neither are the two inseparable as some persons suppose, for a medium of expression can generally be isolated from what is expressed through it.

This book is the direct result of numerous requests from draughtsmen, engineers and teachers for information about the historical development of the engineering drawing language. The complete field of graphics is so large that some limits had to be set and, to avoid wandering off into graphs, charts and general graphical constructions, I have taken as the main theme the representation of three-dimensional objects on a two-dimensional surface. Even so, the story is complex, becoming one of the evolution of ideas, very few of which can be attached absolutely to particular individuals. There are exceptions, of course, and the contributions of Descartes, Desargues, Monge and Farish in particular have been covered.

The material presented has been selected for its general interest and since the book may be used as a work of reference, it has been made as comprehensive as space permits. A number of quotations have been included from original works as being of some value or interest, especially as they are mainly from works not within easy access of most draughtsmen and engineers.

The numbers given in parentheses throughout the text refer to the bibliography at the end of the book.

In my investigations I have received co-operation and help from very many people—practising engineers, professors, and museum and library officials. I would especially like to mention the late George Noble of the Dominion Engineering Co. Ltd., Canada, who played a large part in the standardisation of drawings on the national and international levels, Dr W. Abbott for his encouragement, Mr W. E. Walters, through whom I had my first contact with the history of engineering drawing, Dr D. Pepys Whitely of the Pepysian Library, University of Cambridge, and Professor Wayne L. Shick of the University of Illinois.

Wherever possible drawings are reproduced from the works cited. The remaining drawings, whether copies or originals, are by the author.

Engineering drawing has played and is playing a key role in our civilisation. With roots in art, science and mathematics, it has been both the servant and master of engineering, affecting and being affected by changing technology and organisation. There is probably much more to come; in the meantime I hope these pages have captured some of the past before it is forgotten and lost to the future.

Introducing Shadows and Projection

ACCORDING to a 19th-century encyclopedia, tradition said that 'drawing and sculpture took their rise together when the daughter of Dibutades drew the outline of the shadow of her lover upon a wall, which her father cut out and modelled into a statue'.

The interest of this statement lies not so much in the story itself as in the way that some 19th-century scholars used it to support a theory. By this time the perspective projection had been exhaustively examined and written about in profusion to the point when, to many, drawing and projection were so intimately bound up as to be considered synonymous. Since projection springs from geometrical ideas, and since the ancient Greeks were remarkable geometers, it seemed to these scholars reasonable to presume that perspective projection was known, understood and perhaps even used as early as the times of Pythagoras. So much did they expect this to be true that they grasped every odd piece of information, however vague, which seemed to support this thesis. The story of Dibutades, for instance, invoked the idea of tracing round the outline of a shadow, which was a 'projection' of his daughter's lover.

Today this view has been rejected and the history of perspective applied to pictures is considered as beginning in the Middle Ages. This may seem rather late in mankind's development, but as we shall see more clearly in the next chapter, fundamentally there is no natural, self-evident connection between drawing and projection. From any standpoint, psychological or historical, the concept of projection, especially in making pictures, is an advanced one.

The view held by some 19th-century geometers that the ancient Greeks were familiar with the concept of perspective was not, on the face of it, unreasonable, however. When the Dark Ages descended, nearly all of the ancient Greek writings in Europe disappeared. Fortunately, however, the works of Archimedes, Pythagoras, Euclid, Hero and many others had found their way into the Arabic centres of learning and, as the Arabic area of influence extended, so a knowledge of these early writings spread along the north coast of Africa, then across to Spain by way of the Moors, until they came to Italy.

Early in the 16th century a start was made upon translating these Arabic texts back into Latin, and gradually the Western world rediscovered the science and geometry of the ancient Greeks. This work was continued by scholars over the next 200 years and, by the 19th century, learned men had elucidated enough to be quite astonished by what they found the Greek philosophers had known.

Greek geometry in particular was extremely advanced; indeed one might say that nothing new was added until the time of Descartes. The ancient Greeks certainly had the ability and sufficient geometrical knowledge to develop perspective and if they did not, as seems to be the case, it was probably through a lack of motivation. Since the ancient Greeks' knowledge was found to be so vast and profound, and their ability sufficient to handle ideas more complex to them than perspective, it seemed unreasonable to suppose that this had been neglected. What gave particular substance to this 19th-century view was the stereographic projection. The beginnings of this are obscure, but the motivation, at least, probably lay in astronomy.

Astronomy was a major interest in the early civilisations for many reasons. One of the most important was that the spinning of the earth on its axis was, in effect, the clock denoting the time of day, while the movements of the stars in the heavens gave the calendar for planting seeds or moving animals to new pastures.

The ancient Greeks knew far more than might have been expected about astronomy. Thales of Asia Minor discovered the Solstices and Equinoxes; Anaximander, his friend, discovered that the moon's light was reflected and that the moon revolved about the earth once a month. The phases of the moon were thus explained about 600 B.C. Pythagoras (582–500 B.C.) taught that the earth was a globe which revolved round a central fire, and Aristarchus of Samos discovered the earth's obliquity to the plane of the ecliptic about 250 B.C. In short, by this time it was known that the earth was a globe, that it spun on its axis, that it moved round the sun, that its axis was tilted at $23\frac{1}{2}°$ to the plane of the earth's orbit, and that the moon revolved about the earth. These facts are not unimportant as we shall see in a later chapter.

Knowing this, the ancient astronomers looked beyond the sun and moon, to the planets and stars. Even in primitive times man had learnt to recognise certain constellations and the time naturally came when he found it necessary to map representations of the heavens. Crude drawings were good enough for some purposes, such as simple recognition, but for the science to advance more accurate star maps were required.

In the times we are considering, the heavens were generally supposed to be a number of glass spheres in one of which all the stars were fixed. After devising a method of measuring the positions of stars, the real problem of star map-making was how to represent the surface of a sphere on a flat surface, since this was the only reasonable medium for drawing upon and carrying around. Even if one did not subscribe to the idea of the stars being embedded in a glass sphere, the problem, reduced to the same thing.

Two basic methods were eventually devised; nobody knows exactly from where they came or when, but the ideas of projection have been credited to Apollonius of Perga, next to Archimedes the most illustrious of the ancient Greek geometers, about the year 250 B.C. The two systems became known later as the *orthographic* and *stereographic* projections of the sphere.

Man's earliest ideas of projection no doubt arose from his study of shadows. He soon came to recognise two kinds of projection. There were shadows cast by the sun's rays which were the same size as the object when thrown upon a surface parallel to the object; and there were shadows cast by a candle, effectively a point source of light with diverging rays, giving shadows larger than the objects illuminated. These two lighting systems represent the two fundamental types of projection—parallel and conical.

In ancient Greek times the idea of longitude and latitude were known—they come from words meaning lengths and widths used originally upon small-scale maps, but derived in principle from the very methods used to measure a star's position—and by the projection of a sphere we really mean the projection of a grid of longitude and latitude lines lying on a sphere's surface. In Fig. 1 a simplified hemispherical grid—with circles of latitude at 30° intervals and circles of longitude at 45° intervals—is used to demonstrate parallel and conical projection. In (a) the hemisphere is positioned so that the sun's rays, in casting its shadow on a wall, give an orthographic projection of the sphere. The true form of this shadow or projection is shown in (b) by the full lines. The dotted lines are those of a more complete grid using circles of longitude and latitude at 15° intervals. The main disadvantage of this form of projection for mapping is that as one moves outwards from the centre the grid becomes more and more crowded and the shapes of constellations plotted upon it become badly distorted at the edges. The circles

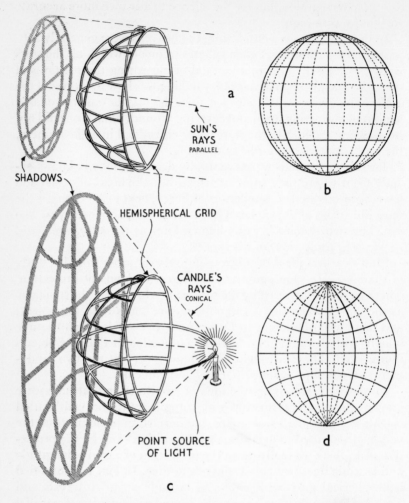

SUN'S
RAYS
PARALLEL

a

SHADOWS

HEMISPHERICAL GRID

b

CANDLE'S
RAYS
CONICAL

POINT SOURCE
OF LIGHT

d

c

Fig. 1. (a) A hemispherical grid used to demonstrate the orthographic projection of a sphere by parallel light rays.

(b) An orthographic projection of a sphere. The full lines are those shown in (a); the dotted ones are additional lines of longitude and latitude.

(c) A hemispherical grid used to demonstrate the stereographic projection of a sphere by a system of conical rays emanating from a point source.

(d) A stereographic projection of a sphere to the same scale as that in (b). The full lines are those shown in (c); the dotted ones are additional lines of longitude and latitude.

Notice that if the point source of light in (c) is moved to the right, the cone of rays becomes more acute; in the limiting position, when the point has reached 'infinity', the conditions of (a) result.

of latitude, being edgewise to the light rays, are projected into straight lines and all the longitude circles are projected into ellipses, except for the outer circle and the central meridian.

In Fig. 1 (c) the same hemisphere is used but this time with a point source of illumination, its position or pole being on the equatorial circle diametrically opposite to the point nearest the plane of projection. The light rays diverge from the point giving a larger shadow. The hemispherical grid is not, however, a plane figure and the various points on the circles are at different distances from the source of illumination, so that the projected shadow is not only different in size, but it is different in shape also. The true shape of this hemisphere's projection is shown in (d) reduced in scale to match (b). This is known as the stereographic projection of the sphere and the ancient Greeks noticed that it had peculiar properties – indeed, they proved these properties by geometrical reasoning. All the projections of the latitude and longitude lines are true arcs of circles and the whole projected grid is a system of orthogonal curves, that is curves which intersect each other at right angles.

At this point, it might be as well for us to make an interesting observation which will help to save much misunderstanding in our study of drawing. The original form of stereographic projection used what we may call a 'primary' geometry – a system of conical rays or projectors in space. The shadow on the wall mentioned above would be produced by this primary geometry. If we placed a camera at the pole point, instead of the candle, and took a photograph, the resulting picture would have been produced by this primary geometry. The candle and the camera do not have to know what shape, shadow or picture to produce; this results automatically from the system of projection.

However, the remarkable properties of the stereographic projection found by the Greeks gave what we may call a 'secondary' geometry – a method of drawing a stereographic grid without recourse to the idea of projection at all. One has only to work out the centres for the various arcs – and this can be accomplished by elementary geometrical constructions – and the whole grid can be drawn with a pair of compasses. This idea of primary and secondary geometries with respect to projections is worth remembering. Whilst the two are connected, in that one may be derived from the other, they are separate in that one can often make a 'picture' using a secondary form of geometry without having any knowledge whatsoever of the original primary geometry. These ideas are very useful in the study

5

of axonometric and perspective projections. Unfortunately the difference between primary and secondary geometries is hardly ever pointed out in drawing-books and considerable mental confusion is caused because the outlines drawn are referred to as 'the projection' irrespective of the method used for drawing them.

How far stereographic projection was used at the time of its invention is difficult to say, but it seems to have been used in planispheres and analemmas. These appear in both ancient Greek and Arabic writings[16,17]*, although their true nature is not always clear because both terms were used loosely, sometimes for an instrument based on projections, and sometimes as a synonym for projections. A planisphere in its simplest form consists of two parts; a flat sheet upon which is marked a projection of the stars in the heavens, and a second flat sheet with a circular (more often elliptical) hole in it, the edge of which represents the horizon at some particular location. The second sheet is mounted so that it can revolve on a centre over the star map; when turned to certain marked positions, that part of the map showing through the hole depicts the stars to be seen at certain hours and times of the year at that place. Instruments of this nature demanded a great deal of theoretical geometrical and astronomical knowledge and exhibit the remarkable progress made in the early civilisations.

Claudius Ptolemaeus, or Ptolemy (c. A.D. 90–168), was an Egyptian astronomer and geographer who was keen on mapping the known world. The world was known to be a sphere–indeed, Eratosthenes (c. 275–194 B.C.) had succeeded in calculating its size, his radius being within 500 miles of the true figure–and Ptolemy used stereographic projection for this purpose (amongst other projections). Although the earth's surface was on the outside of a sphere and the stars were, supposedly, on the inside of one, the general problem was the same–the representing of a spherical surface on a flat surface. In geographical map-making the original projectional basis of the stereographic projection is really forgotten; the lines are used merely as a convenient grid to work upon–that is, they may not only be drawn by a secondary kind of geometry, but they may be thought of in this way also.

Mapping has only a fringe connection with our subject, but astronomy, on the other hand, has a direct bearing, for the theories created to account for the apparent motions of the sun, moon and

---

* These figures, and other similar ones throughout the text, refer to the numbered authorities listed in the bibliography.

stars provided the fundamental basis for the art of sun-dialling, which we shall pursue later.

Ptolemy had associations with the library at Alexandria and, besides contributing much himself to astronomy and geography, he edited many of the earlier Greek geometrical works in making translations. Unfortunately, Ptolemy is also well known for initiating a retrograde step; he put forward the Geocentric Theory in which the earth was a stationary globe around which the heavenly bodies moved. His reason for rejecting the earlier theories was that if the earth spun on its axis tremendous winds would be created which would blow everything movable off the earth. This was, perhaps, the beginning of the Dark Ages; later, even the spherical nature of the earth was largely abandoned in favour of a flat earth. It was nearly 1300 years before Copernicus (1473–1543) exposed the fallacies in the Ptolemaic system and reverted to the original Greek ideas.

One may well be able to see now why the 19th-century view of the beginnings of perspective – and thus, to them, drawing – were centred on ancient Greece. The Greeks had found out so much which had to be rediscovered almost 2000 years later that it was hardly conceivable that they could have missed the theory of perspective – especially when the stereographic projection was a very special form of perspective projection. In taking this view, however, the scholars failed to understand the real nature of drawing and the differences in motivation between the Greek artists and those of the late Middle Ages.

2

The Fundamental Nature of Drawing

TO KNOW why the ancient Greeks probably did not use their geometrical genius to develop perspective projection, we need to forget much of what we know today and consider the nature of pictures in a more elementary sense. This is worthwhile for many reasons, not least because it allows us to look at old drawings from a sensible viewpoint.

Because, as adults, we have been in contact with drawings for most of our lives in the form of plans, photographs, printed illustrations and so on, we have learnt how to interpret these in an almost unconscious way. If, however, we are to have any real understanding of the nature of drawing and the stages through which mankind has climbed, we have to go back somewhat, forgetting what we already know, or think we know, about drawing, to some fundamental ideas of this basic language—and it is basic, for even the characters used to print this book and most other symbols stem from pictures of one sort or another.

To understand roughly the mechanism we use in drawing it is not necessary for us to delve deeply into psychology; a purely superficial treatment based on a crude model will be perfectly suitable for our requirements.

Drawing depends upon seeing and interpreting or analysing. This process is demonstrated in Fig. 2. (a) is a letter W which has to be copied. A very young child drew it as in (b). For the purpose of this discussion we can consider the child's eye to be physiologically as developed as the adult eye. Both receive the same light impulses. True, the child may not be able to control its hand as fully as when grown up, but the real difference lies in the powers of analysis. In the original W the child sees merely four lines and their approximate orientation. It interprets the symbol it has drawn to a similar degree and the resemblance between the two is of a most rudimentary nature.

A similar copying process carried out by a child of 10 resulted in (c). Here the copier recognised that two of the strokes were thicker than the others and that the outer strokes were topped by serifs.

An average untrained adult might reach the stage shown in (d). This is very much nearer the truth. The angles of slope are not in themselves recognised, although the parallelism of lines is perceived.

a   b   c   d   e

Fig. 2. (a) A letter 'W'.

(b) A very young child's attempt at copying the letter; it displays only the very basic attributes—four lines and their approximate directions and points of joining.

(c) An older child's copying attempt; there is little improvement on the former in geometrical quality, but the copier is aware of further attributes—the thicker strokes and the serifs.

(d) An untrained adult's copy of the letter 'W'; the concept of parallelism is used here, but there is some misjudging of proportions and the left and right slopes are not symmetrical.

(e) Apart from comparative lengths and overall size, this shows the angles, widths and lengths which have to be noted and taken into account in making the copy.

The upper point of the W is not noticed as being in line with the serifs and the copier has seen something which is not, in fact, there— feeling that there should be some order, he has made the serifs of equal length. This is misperception; seeing what one thinks one ought to see or jumping to a conclusion.

With some drawing training, one might eventually analyse this letter as in (e) and so draw it properly. It is worth noting that, left on their own, very few persons ever reach the stage when they can properly analyse and so draw even one letter of the alphabet. This letter W, for instance, requires one to notice that the angles A are equal, and also to judge the value of A possibly by the easier expedient of gauging the distances between the tops of the strokes and dropping verticals; one also has to notice the thick strokes and judge their thickness, to notice the parallelism between strokes, and to recognise that there is order about the serifs, the 'overhanging' pieces being of equal lengths rather than the complete serifs.

To notice all these things one must have built up conscious concepts of angles, of parallelism, of equality, of straightness and so on. In short, we see things in terms of what we already know and understand.

We can make a rough diagrammatic representation of this copying process as in Fig. 3. The starting-point is an object—here just a letter W—from which light travels to the eye, a process here called transmission. The eye converts this light into nervous impulses

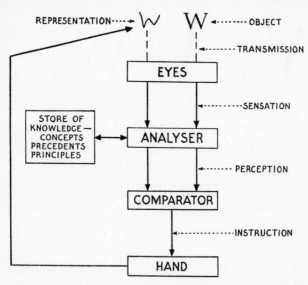

Fig. 3. A schematic arrangement of the copying process. The comparison between original and copy is made at the stage of perception or the level of conscious understanding; it is not a mechanical comparison of two optical images.

which are sent to the brain, a process sometimes referred to as sensation. Whatever may be the real nature of the brain, for our purposes it is sufficient to consider it as three units—an analyser, a store and a comparator. We have already seen that we tend to analyse the shapes we see and the completeness of this process is dependent upon what knowledge, ideas, experience, images or associations are already in the mental store. The result we get from the analyser is what we call perception and, whereas we may all have identical sensations, our degrees and even kinds of perceptions may differ radically. It all depends upon what we have in our mental store. A child will not notice that two lines are parallel until it understands the nature of parallelism. Parallelism in its most elementary form means two lines with equal distance between them at all points; this, of course, needs the more basic ideas of straightness, of distance and equality to be perceived. Slowly, very slowly if unaided, the brain builds up more and more complex patterns to which it, in a sense, gives names.

After perception, the brain can give instructions to the hand which controls the copying instrument, a pencil, say. What is drawn also sends light signals to the eye, which pass through similar stages–sensation and perception–to reach what I have called the comparator. Here the analysis of what is drawn is compared with the analysis of the original object; any difference can cause the hand to make corrections. I say 'can' because the result does not necessarily follow; the copier may be aware of differences but not care. Much depends upon whether the drawing is for the draughtsman's own benefit–that is, to aid his thinking–or whether it is to be exhibited to others–that is, used for communication. Who the others might be can also affect the result. In looking at drawings from the past it is useful to try to ascertain the purpose the artist or draughtsman had in mind, otherwise there is little standard for judging the work.

The important thing to notice in the above discussion is that comparison takes place only after perception. We are, therefore, not coldly comparing transmissions of light, or sensations, but we are comparing what the brain *thinks* about the two sets of stimuli. We are comparing the results of our analyses or perceptions. This is the reason why artists can produce such dissimilar results when working from the same model. Each one's perception depends upon what they have taken from their mental store for the analysis process, and this is partly a function of what has previously been put into the store. I say 'partly' because whereas an ordinary person is undiscriminative and his perception is almost wholly a function of what is in the store, artists are selective in their choice which allows them to 'see things in different ways'.

It is, indeed, this process of analysis which allows us to recognise anything or anybody. More particular, this process allows us to recognise various *attributes* of any shape or object and so allows us to represent them in drawings. Literally, the only copy one can make of, say, a door is another door. One can, however, make a kind of copy on paper by representing the essential attributes of a door in such a way that the brain's analysis of the door and the drawing of the door agree in so far as the analysis goes. In copying attributes one must needs be selective; a simple outline drawing not only ignores solidity, but also colour and texture, although this still allows us to recognise what is represented if our powers of analysis are sufficiently developed.

This analysing process is always functioning, for without it we should be unable to recognise anything, neither could we learn, as learning is largely a case of building up more and more complex ideas from the patterns we already recognise. We could follow up this extensively, but it will suffice if we note how complicated is the process of seeing – and drawing is intimately bound up with seeing.

Fig. 4. A child's drawing of his home-made trolley. It displays all the essential characteristics – the body has a bottom and sides, but no top; it runs on two wheels (two closed curves connected to a point inside each by spokes) and is pulled by two shafts on the front.

Having now some understanding of how we draw, we can turn our attention to the real core of the drawing process, in as much as it affects our subject. We cannot conveniently deal with, store or carry around with us three-dimensional objects or models, and drawing is essentially a transformation of solid objects or space relationships into a two-dimensional medium – that is, putting a representation of them onto paper.

The evolution of ideas which influence drawing techniques throughout the ages of mankind are, to a limited extent, experienced by us all as we grow up and by studying the graphical efforts of children we can see some of the stages through which our ancestors passed.

Fig. 4 shows a drawing of a trolley made by a young child. His father – with much more advanced concepts – asked the child why he had not drawn a line across the top. The child replied contemptuously, 'Don't be silly! That's where I get in'. As sophisticated adults, who have presumably left all this behind us, we might not think much of this effort. Let us remember, however, that the child is not comparing the visual sensations arising from his trolley with those of the drawing, but he is comparing his analyses of the two – comparing

Fig. 5. A child's drawing displaying the essential attributes of a house and garden. In the case of mother, the attributes are only those of a woman and a word is added to complete the act of communication.

two perceptions. With very limited knowledge and experience, the child has made a very commendable effort. In fact, the order of the analysis can best be seen by putting it into words. The trolley has a bottom and sides, but no top. It has two wheels on the bottom and two shafts on the front. The drawing of the trolley can be described in exactly the same terms. At this level of analysis the drawing is an adequate representation of the object and the child is quite satisfied.

In ordinary general cases children overcome the problem of

Fig. 6. A drawing by a child of 10 with no formal training; whilst this appears to show apparent shapes rather than true shapes, it is an extension of the technique used in Fig. 5 except that the corner of the road—drawn as a true right angle—is placed at an angle. This is similar to planometric projection used by architects, although the child is not conscious of such advanced concepts.

representing three-dimensional arrangements very easily. We have all seen drawings like Fig. 5. The nearest objects – all very simply represented–are at the bottom of the picture and further objects are lifted up the paper. There is no ambiguity in the child's mind in showing the side of the house and the plan of the garden in one plane. It knows that, standing at the end of the garden, one can see the house and the garden together; the garden is known to be rectangular in shape and so is the front of the house, and the latter is at the further end of the garden. All these simple attributes are represented quite clearly. The hedge, the fence and the trees are all depicted by representations of their essential attributes. The exception, perhaps, is mother who has her name written underneath. This is not simply a case of adding a title. The representation of mother simply shows the attributes of a woman–head, arms, legs and a skirt on the body: unless mother has some visual attribute which is peculiar to her and can be represented, the only way left to be more specific is to add a recognisable attribute which is not, in our sense, visual–the word 'mother'.

This latter idea is of more than passing interest. Soon we shall see how the ancients were led to the same device and, in due course, we shall see how words had to be used on engineering drawings to represent attributes which cannot be shown in terms of shape.

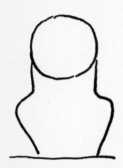

Fig. 7. A child's drawing of a vase; an attempt to display three basic attributes–roundness, symmetry and the flatness of the bottom.

The method of depicting 'depth' in pictures by raising objects up the page is a natural, deep-rooted one, but drawing things as they 'are'–or simply analysing what is seen and then making outlines with the same attributes–has its limitations and there comes a time when children are baffled by a conflict. Drawing a vase raises this issue very well. The child draws a circle for the top of the vase as in Fig. 7, since the top is recognised to be circular. Shape is also perceived in the sides of the vase which are seen to be symmetrical–another basic concept, incidentally. The vase stands on a table; its bottom is flat so it is drawn as a straight line. In time the intelligent child begins to feel the inadequacy of this representation and asks daddy or teacher what is wrong with it. The conflict arises because the child knows that the base is also circular as well as flat; and for that matter, the top is flat as well as circular, since the vase will stand turned upside down.

The problem in general terms is one of how to represent on paper an object which has shape in more than one 'direction'. There are two fundamental answers to this problem; one is to retain the idea of true shape and exhibit the many shapes in an object by using a number of drawings of the object as seen from various directions; the other is to keep the idea of 'one object, one drawing', but transform its real shapes into apparent shapes.

Whilst we accept these today, it is worth noting that whereas children reach this critical point quite naturally, they only go beyond it by virtue of instruction or by seeing examples in printed illustrations. Neither of these two concepts is easy and their introduction and development is the next part of our story.

3

Representing Attributes in Drawings

THERE are, of course, an immense number of drawings and paintings from the past available to us. In many ways it is unrepresentative to select a mere handful for discussion, but it is reasonable to do so in this context as our aim is distinctly limited – to show the empirical stages of drawing which preceded those in which ideas of projection were introduced.

Fig. 8. Bronze Age plough; a rock engraving of about 1500 B.C. from Fontanalba, Italian Alps, height about one foot. This was probably not intended as a work of art, but as a diagram displaying the arrangement of oxen and harness. It shows clearly this arrangement whilst the details are symbolic, that is, they depict sufficient attributes to be recognisable.

Fig. 8 is a cave drawing, or really a rock engraving, from Fontanalba in the Italian Alps, reputed to have been made about 1500 B.C. It portrays a Bronze Age plough in a style easily matched with children's drawings. Whether one considers this to be crude or not depends upon whether one thinks of it as a picture or as a diagram. Its purpose may well have been simply to display how beasts of burden were harnessed to pull a plough; it may, in fact, be nearer to a technical drawing than to a picture in the sense understood today. The beasts of burden are simply depicted as large masses with horns – two of their obvious attributes. These animals are connected in pairs by something rigid – a piece of wood probably – fixed to each in the region of the neck. These crosspieces are then joined by some other element which is extended and attached to the plough. The lower markings may be an attempt to show a man in plan view guiding the plough. The man driving the animals is more clearly seen as a 'matchstick' figure. This, again, is reminiscent of children's efforts; it displays head, body, arms and legs, the essential characteristics of a man.

The ancient Egyptian in Fig. 9 is drilling a hole with a bow drill.

This drawing is similar to many executed on the walls of tombs, and shows some other drawing characteristics which appeared in most civilisations at the appropriate time. The attributes of a human face are more simply displayed in profile view; the legs are also better drawn in side view because the bending of the legs appears in true form. The shape of the torso, on the other hand, is generally more recognisable from the front and this makes it easier to represent the two arms naturally. There are, of course, exceptions, but for these reasons most drawings of people in this stage are contrived so that the middle part of the figure is twisted—side view of head, front view of torso, and side view of legs. The other pictures in Fig. 9 are from the Mosaic Standard from Ur and illustrate the same kind of technique as practised by the Babylonians about 2500 B.C.

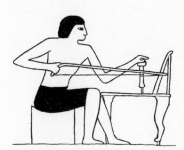

Fig. 9. *Left*: Typical ancient Egyptian tomb drawing.
   Right: Two parts of the Mosaic Standard from Ur, about 2500 B.C. now in British Museum.
   Both use the characteristic method of drawing the human form by showing the head from the side, the shoulders and torso from the front and the legs from the side—the easiest way of showing the basic shapes of these parts.

A slightly more advanced stage is shown in Plate 1. This is from ancient Greece and has been dated about 530 B.C., that is, contemporary with Pythagoras. It shows Achilles slaying the Queen of the Amazons. Again, notice the faces in profile, the torsos viewed square on, and the legs in side view. There is considerably more detail in this picture although it is based on the earlier conventions, if they may be called that. Since all warriors looked much alike, as with children's drawings, words are distributed over the picture to make sure the viewer is quite clear on what or who is represented.

   It is of interest to note that most early pictures were concerned with people; when things were depicted it was because they were being used by persons. Indeed, although it is rash to generalise, one might go as far as to say that early drawings are mainly concerned with events, stories or actions. People, therefore, played a prominent part, and this is probably one important reason why the Greeks did not develop perspective projection although they were advanced in geometry. There was little, or no, motivation.

Throughout mankind's history one finds that the philosophers– today the scientists–follow up logically the work of those empiricists who have the motivation but not the rigorous kind of knowledge from appropriate fields to advance it. Undoubtedly if the ancient Greek artists had embarked on the portrayal of *things*, with geometrical shapes, rather than *people*, with complex flowing forms, a situation would have arisen in which their able geometers would have seen the problems and provided answers.

As it was, with the fall of the Greek and Roman civilisations Europe entered the Dark Ages. Much of the Greek and Roman learning, however, was taken eastwards by refugees where it was progressively translated into Arabic. As the centuries passed the Arabic civilisation spread westwards along the northern coast of Africa and eventually across the Straits of Gibraltar into Spain. By this route the works of Euclid, Archimedes, Apollonius of Perga, Ptolemy and others were re-found by the Western world, and translated back into Latin. This gave some of the groundwork for future progress, although the empirical efforts of artists, who had become ever more ambitious, had set the scene, as we shall see.

A picture of the 15th century from an Arabic source is shown in Plate 2. This is a more detailed version of the technique used in the last chapter by the child to depict the house and garden. In general the buildings are shown in front view and their positions are denoted by raising the further ones higher up the picture. The artist got into some difficulties here and there. On the right the buildings just go on and on for the extent of the picture; on the left, sky has been introduced, and not being clear where this should end it has just been 'faded out'. The treatment is not consistent throughout– just as it is not in children's drawings where the idea is to represent recognisable attributes. Here and there one can see attempts at depicting apparent shapes, such as in the gate at the upper left and the square tower below the lower boat.

Some of the real difficulties came in the representation of complicated machinery–complicated at the time, although elementary to us. Fig 10 has been labelled by some writers as a 'one plane projection'. As we have seen, however, such a drawing had no projectional basis at all. The artist has tried to represent the geometrical truths–the objects' attributes–which she has recognised. If we describe the machine in terms of words we can see to what extent this drawing tallies with reality. The top, which supports the grindstones, is square, and this in turn is supported on four columns or legs fixed to horizontal timbers as a base. Running horizontally through the structure is a shaft to which is fixed a toothed wheel

Fig. 10. Drawing of an Undershot Water Mill. The original was in a manuscript on vellum with 636 drawings compiled by the Abbess Herrad of Landsperg about 1160 as an instructive collection for her pupils. The MS., called 'Hortus-Deliciarum', was burnt in 1870 and the only remains are a few drawings which had been copied by scholars. This drawing is not based upon any conceptions of projection but is a recording of a number of geometrical 'truths'.

under the grindstones and a water-wheel outside the structure. The corn is fed into the centre of the grindstones through a hopper on top, and the stones are turned by a lantern pinion rotated by the toothed wheel. All these facts, and others, are displayed.

As with all empirically produced drawings, there are inconsistencies. The two circles of the toothed wheel represent in fact two concentric circles. The two main circles of the water-wheel, however, have to be interpreted differently. These represent circles of the same size, but they were drawn this way otherwise they would coincide and the artist would not have known how to represent the paddles which connect the two circles. The representation of the grindstones by two concentric circles is probably also meant to convey that one is above the other. Here we see size, especially comparative size, sacrificed to show other attributes which the artist considered more important. This is quite usual in drawings of this period, and whilst we can often reconstruct the machines depicted in principle, we have to use our own imagination in assessing the real size of parts.*

The four columns on their timber bases are interesting as they can lead us on quickly to the next stage. They are re-drawn in Fig. 11 (a). Here we have two identical U-shapes, but the artist did not deal with these as she did the identical circular shapes; she raised

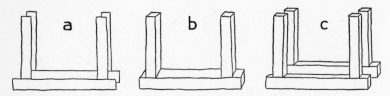

Fig. 11. Stages in development of representing timber bulks.

the further one up the drawing and displaced it laterally. Now suppose the space between these U-shapes was filled in with a succession of timbers, the solid mass becomes as represented in Fig. 11 (b) and this leads to the recognition – checked by observation – that one can invariably see three faces of a piece of timber at once. Immediately one sees how to give such shapes the appearance of solidity and in later drawings these two U-shapes are displayed generally as in Fig. 11 (c).

An example showing this stage is the drawing of a trébuchet, or stone-throwing machine of war, illustrated in Fig. 12. This is dated about 1405 and it shows the recognition of another principle – that objects further away appear to be smaller than nearer objects. At first sight one might consider that the artist was making a rather poor attempt at a perspective drawing. He may have been, but the evidence is rather against this. A trébuchet was a large machine, often up to 30 feet high and the view shown is not a natural one.

* Where people were concerned, their size in old pictures is usually a measure of their importance, kings and pharaohs being drawn larger than workers or slaves.

Instead we may consider this as a separate stage in drawing which paved the way for the introduction of perspective. Here we see the three developments merged into a composite representation. Various parts are laid out laterally and vertically to show lengths and heights; other parts are drawn behind these, made smaller and raised up the picture to depict depth. The solidity of the timbers is shown by drawing them with two or three faces in view, as may

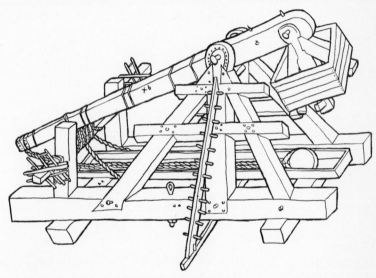

Fig. 12. A line drawing based on a painting in the University of Göttingen Library of about 1405. It shows a trébuchet, a military stone-throwing machine of the Middle Ages. The proportions are only approximately correct.

be appropriate, but there is a lack of consistency in handling this technique—sometimes the timbers are displayed according to the above conventions whilst sometimes the appearance of the timbers is more as they would be seen by an artist at ground level.

This drawing is representative of the last stage in development from simply depicting obvious attributes; true shapes have become progressively replaced by apparent shapes until the picture is almost like the view of a real object seen through a window.

When this stage had been reached, the portrayal of views naturally, or as we say today in perspective, became a serious topic of study by artists, particularly those in Italy, where painting was flourishing in the 15th and 16th centuries. Pietro del Borgo, using, it seems, the window idea, eventually laid down certain rules which he arrived at by supposing objects to be placed on a transparent tablet; he then endeavoured to trace the images which rays of light emitting from them would make upon the plane or tablet. Thus, nearly a thousand years after the great Greek geometers the connection between pictures and projection was established.

4

Perspective : Projection Applied to Pictures

PERSPECTIVE projection is not a primary medium for modern engineering drawings, and in consequence, we shall not follow its history very far. Our aim is to expand logically the principle of 'one object, one drawing' – which called for representation on paper in terms of apparent rather than real shapes – and to introduce certain ideas about projection which affected other lines of thought.

Although in the last chapter we were turning our attention to the drawing of machines, most painters of the Middle Ages were still concerned with illustrating stories or deeds. Most of their attention had been focused on people and animals, buildings and other items displayed being of secondary importance.

Once the idea of a picture as a 'window' was accepted a very obvious way of drawing a scene was apparent. If the artist could view the scene from one invariable position – such as by looking through a hole in a piece of wood mounted on a stand – and place a piece of glass between himself and the view, he could trace the outlines of the scene onto the glass. These outlines could then be traced onto a canvas and painted over to give the picture. Albrecht Dürer did, in fact, use this method for making portraits, and he has left us an engraving showing himself using this apparatus (Fig. 13). The very word 'perspective' comes from the Medieval Latin word 'perspectiva' which itself was derived from Latin roots meaning 'through –looking – of the nature of' or 'as looking through'.

The outlines formed on the glass were, in principle, the same as we would capture today by taking a photograph with a camera. They were formed by what was earlier called the primary geometry, that is by a large number of light rays in space converging to a point source, the artist's eye, the picture being formed by the intersection of these rays with the glass or picture plane.

Artists, however, really wanted a secondary form of geometry to work with; that is, a set of rules which would allow them to build up pictures from imagination. In other words they wanted to make pictures of scenes which might not exist in reality, but in such a way that the pictures would still appear as 'windows' through

23

which one could view the scenes. As with stereographic projection, the secondary geometry, or system of rules to be applied on paper, was derivable from the primary geometry. Some of these rules appeared fairly obvious from the start; others were only found after a long time had elapsed and many thinkers had devoted much time and effort.

Fig. 13. A reproduction of a woodcut by Dürer of about 1500. It shows the artist with one eye at a fixed point while he traces onto the glass screen the apparent outlines of the sitter.

Paolo Uccello (1397–1475) has often been credited with developing the first principles of perspective. Giorgio Vasari, writing in 1547, wrote the following:

Paolo Uccello would have been the most delightful and imaginative genius since Giotto that had adorned the art of painting, if he had devoted as much pains to figures and animals as he did to questions of perspective for, although these are ingenious and good in their way, yet an immoderate devotion to them causes an infinite waste of time . . . and clogs the mind with difficulties. . . . But Paolo, without ever wasting a moment, was always attracted by the most difficult things of art, and brought to perfection the method of representing buildings, to the tops of their cornices and roofs, in perspective from their plans and elevations. This was done by intersecting lines, diminishing at the centre; the point of view, whether high or low, being first decided. He laboured so hard over these difficulties that he invented a method and rules for planting figures firmly on their feet and for their gradual foreshortening and diminution in proportion as they recede, a matter that was previously left to chance. . . . When engaged upon these matters Paolo would remain alone, like a hermit, with hardly any intercourse, for weeks and months, not allowing himself to be seen. . . . He left . . . a wife who used to say that Paolo would remain the night long in his study to work out the lines of his perspective, and that when she called him to come to rest, he replied, 'Oh, what a sweet thing this perspective is!' And in truth, if it was sweet to him, his labours have rendered it no less dear and useful to those who have practised it after him.[73]*

Paolo was something of a mathematician, and the effect it had upon him was probably that of mathematical beauty, which ordinary artists, such as Vasari, usually do not understand. And so, through some sheer, almost fanatical, compulsion, perspective, as we now understand it, was born.

Artists of the 15th and 16th centuries simplified their problem very cleverly, using a development of Uccello's ideas which had already reached a state of 'perfection'. One could imagine people, buildings and other objects standing upon an imaginary chequerboard, or squared pavement. If one could make a perspective representation of this pavement in a picture, then one could place the various items in the picture on the appropriate 'square', and the apparent size of the object or person could be gauged as being proportional to the apparent size of the 'square' upon which it was drawn. Whether Fig. 14, showing an early screw-cutting lathe (middle 16th century), was drawn by this method or not is difficult to tell; the squared floor may have been added simply for decoration, the artist having seen other perspective pictures drawn upon such squaring. However, this illustration demonstrates how such a picture could be made.

How was such a 'fictitious pavement'† to be produced on paper? The general method seems to have been as follows. It had been

* Drawings by Uccello are reproduced in Kline's *Mathematics in Western Culture*; nineteen reproductions of works of great artists are here used in another approach to the story of perspective.

† This is the expression used by Alberti in describing the method; see Fig. 15.

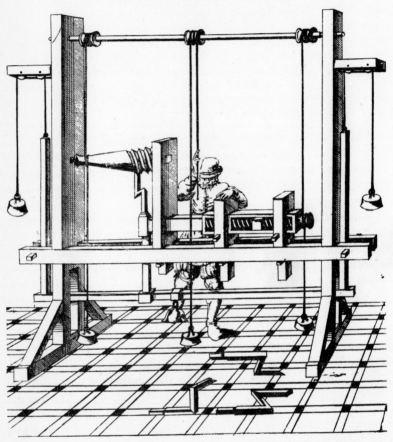

Fig. 14. Besson's Screw-Cutting Lathe: one of a number of drawings of Besson's apparatus published after his death about 1568.

The drawing is in perspective, superimposed upon a squared 'pavement'. Whether this 'pavement' was used to construct this particular drawing is doubtful.

observed that if one looked down a long straight road, the two parallel edges appeared to meet in a point directly in front of one. This phenomenon was made use of very easily. If the rectangle in Fig. 15 (a) was the border of the picture, the central point could be marked as *f*, this point being directly in front of one. At the bottom

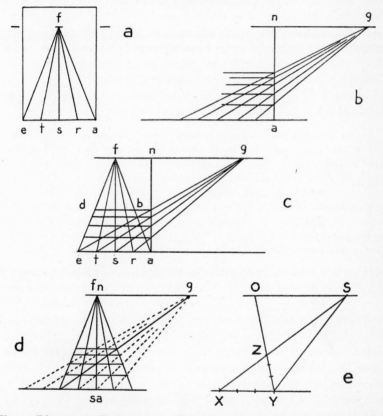

Fig. 15. Diagrams to illustrate the early development of perspective. The central figure is from the works of Leonardo da Vinci. The upper drawings have been reconstructed from a verbal account given by Leone Battista Alberti in 1435.

of the picture, the points *e, t, s, r, a*, etc. would be marked off so that the divisions represented some unit of measurement, and each of these points could then be joined to *f*, which would lie on the horizon in the picture. To complete the picture of the pavement squares, a number of horizontal lines had to be positioned. This was done on a separate sheet as in Fig. 15 (b). This represents a side view of the picture plane, *na*, with the artist's eye at *g*. The lower horizontal line represents the ground, and this is marked off in equal divisions as was the ground line, or bottom of the picture, in (a). Each of these divisions is then connected by a series of converging lines to the eye at *g*. These represent the light rays reaching the eye from the transverse divisions of the pavement and where they intersect *na* gives their apparent positions in the picture.

Leone Battista Alberti has left us in *De re Aedificateria* (1435) one of the earliest accounts of this method, although today there are no illustrations to go with the text. Dürer and Leonardo da Vinci enlarged upon Alberti's writings and provided drawings – (c) in Fig. 15 is taken from the work of da Vinci and it is simply (b) superimposed upon (a). About this Leonardo wrote:

If you draw the plan of a square (in perspective) and tell me the length of the near side, and if you mark within it a point at random, I shall be able to tell you how far is your sight from that square and what is the position of the selected point. You must proceed as follows: Produce *ab* and *de* to intersect in *f*. This point *f* gives you the height of the eye. If you wish to know the distance, draw the division *an* and the line *eg*. Its intersection with *gf* gives the distance point. Then join the marks *a, r, s, t, e,* to the point *f* and to the point *g*. Scale your drawing and you will see the position of your point marked at random in the square.

This is a very early example of the science of photogrammetry, which was developed early this century to elucidate true information from photographs – that is, to work perspective 'backwards'.

There are a number of ways of superimposing (b) on (a) apart from that shown in Fig. 15 (c). A much more interesting superimposition is that demonstrated in (d) where the side view of the picture plane, *na*, is in coincidence with the central point, *f*. This, of course, gives precisely the same results as (c) but it throws up an interesting property hinted at by Alberti. The lines emanating from point *g* become the diagonals of the squares in the picture. In particular, one such line, shown solid, is the diagonal of the large containing square as well as of the four smaller squares which lie on it. In practice, then, only this one line needed to be drawn, for where it cut the lines running to the centre of vision, *f*, gave the points through which to draw the transverse lines.

This property – and much else which sprang from it – seems to have puzzled many artists and geometers at the time, although they made good use of it whatever their depth of understanding. For instance, one could generalise this property as in (e), so that one could place any point into a picture – providing it was on the ground – without drawing a squared pavement.

The lines in Fig. 15 (e) are extracted from (d) and the whole may be explained thus. Suppose that the line XY produced is the ground line, that is, the line where the picture plane meets the ground. Consider now a point on this ground line Y, and behind the picture plane a point Z three units away, measured perpendicularly from Y. To find the position of Z in the picture, as shown, a number of steps are taken. Firstly, Y is joined to O, the centre of vision. Since all lines perpendicular to the ground line appear to meet at O, Z must lie on YO. Secondly S is positioned so that OS represents the distance of the viewer from the picture plane. Three units are then marked off from Y to give point X. X is joined to S cutting YO in the required point Z. This must be so, because comparing the lines in (e) with their counterparts in (d), the desired point is three 'squares' from the left of the latter and three 'squares' into the picture.

Many artists in the Middle Ages seem to have been somewhat confused over the nature of this property, although they used it extensively in their work. The difficulty lay not so much in the construction, which could be reduced to a number of rules and carried out by rote, but in the interpretation of what the lines represented. In Fig. 15 (d) one can still interpret the lines emanating from g as visual rays cutting the picture plane in side view, na. Although in (e) the lines shown are extracted from those in (d) it is difficult to interpret them in the same way. There is no side view of the picture plane, and the lines XS and YS can hardly be considered as visual rays. What could they be considered as, then?

There are two ways of thinking about this and, over a period of time, one concept became replaced with another. For our own understanding we can follow these steps in the next illustration. Fig. 16 (a) is a pictorial representation of Fig. 15 (a). Here we have the vertical picture plane, the eye's position, a number of longitudinal lines receding from the picture plane, and the picture or perspective view of these lines running to the centre of vision, f. In (b) we see a vertical plane introduced through point g, the eye's position. Visual rays extending from the transverse lines on the ground intersect the picture plane to give the picture or perspective view of these lines. The longitudinal and transverse lines added together, of course, gave the squared pavement as shown in (c). This illustration also shows the vertical plane containing g revolved flat into the

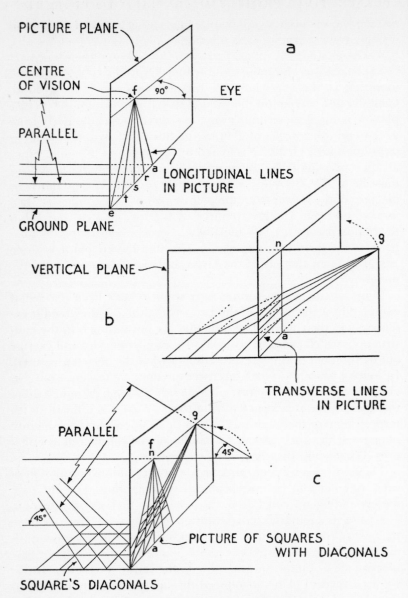

PICTURE PLANE

CENTRE
OF VISION

PARALLEL

GROUND PLANE

LONGITUDINAL LINES
IN PICTURE

EYE

a

VERTICAL PLANE

b

TRANSVERSE LINES
IN PICTURE

PARALLEL

PICTURE OF SQUARES
WITH DIAGONALS

c

SQUARE'S DIAGONALS

Fig. 16. Demonstrating the ideas behind the stages in Fig. 15.
  (a) Positioning the longitudinal lines on the picture plane.
  (b) Positioning the transverse lines on the picture plane.
  (c) Combination of (a) and (b). Point *g* can be considered as the eye's position revolved into the picture plane with visual rays running to it, or as a special vanishing point for lines running at 45 degrees to the picture plane.

picture plane to give the equivalent of Fig. 15 (d). The combination of Figs. 16 (a) and (b) is the first interpretation of (c). There is, however, another way of looking at the latter illustration.

The centre of vision, point f, is what has become known as a vanishing point. It is the point on the picture plane at which the parallel lines on the ground appear to meet, as viewed from that particular position of the eye. It is found at the intersection of the picture plane with a line running from the eye parallel to the lines on the ground.

The diagonals of the pavement squares may be looked upon in the same way; they are also a set of parallel lines which appear to meet at a certain point, a point which, again, may be found at the intersection of the picture plane with a line from the eye parallel to the diagonals on the ground, that is, at 45 degrees.

Point g, therefore, could be looked upon as the position of the artist's eye swung round, for convenience, into the picture plane—in which case the lines running from it represented visual rays—or as a special vanishing point—in which case the same lines could be regarded as the picture of a set of parallel lines running at 45 degrees to the picture plane. The confusion which existed, therefore, rested simply on the fact that there were two interpretations for one set of lines drawn on paper. In the earlier works the first concept prevailed, g being called the 'eye' and f sometimes 'the other eye'. In later books, g was given a special name 'the distance point' (today known as a measuring point), because it allowed one to place points into the picture in the 'depth' dimension.

The second interpretation, which could be used as in Fig. 15 (e) to place isolated points into a picture, led to the abandonment of the squared pavement idea (although it was revived again in the 19th century) and to the development of perspective as we know it today.

It is impossible to record the very many persons who played some part in this development, but the following are the more important names: Albrecht Dürer (1471–1528), Viator (Jean Pélerin or Viator of Toul) (1445–1524), Vignola (Jacopo Barazzo of Vignola) (*c.* 1550), John Cousin (*c.* 1560), Serlio (*c.* 1540) and Guido Ubaldus (Guidobaldo) (1600). Two other persons must also be mentioned—Samuel Marolois and Gérard Desargues.

Samuel Marolois published an extensive work on perspective in Amsterdam in 1629. This was no mean effort by any standards or for any time. Besides a substantial text, this work contained about

200 double-page engravings with perspective renderings not only of buildings and general objects of a box-like nature, but also such complicated things as spiral staircases. He even used horizontal picture planes to give views looking up or down stair wells, and

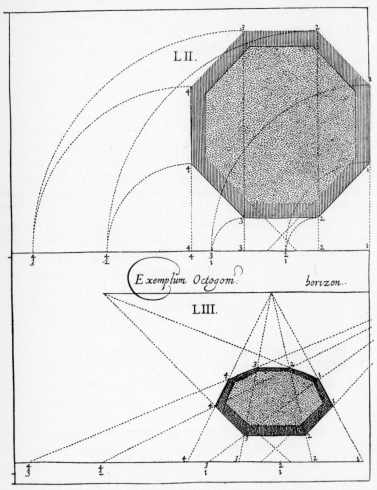

Fig. 17. Figures 52 and 53 of Marolois's *La Perspective* of 1629.

technical illustrators might be interested to know that he went so far as to suggest the use of perspective grids.

Two illustrations from Samuel Marolois's work are given here (and another appears in the following chapter). Fig. 17 shows at

PLATE I

Achilles slaying the Queen of the Amazons as depicted on an Attic Black-
figured Amphora of about 540 B.C.

City of Baghdad in Flood; from an Anthology produced at Shirwan
in 1468.

the top the plan of an octagon; below is a perspective rendering of it. The method used is that shown in principle in Fig. 15 (e). There is no need for us to consider the construction in detail; basically, one can see that any point is considered to be at the intersection of two lines—one at right angles to the picture plane and one at 45 degrees. These lines are drawn in perspective, running respectively to the centre of vision and the distance point S (off the diagram to the right), their intersection giving the point's position in the picture.

Marolois did not follow just one line of development and amongst the other avenues he followed was that shown in principle in Fig. 18. This is incorporated here because it was subsequently largely forgotten and Monge reintroduced it 170 years later as his own invention. This sort of thing often happens in history; principles are discovered independently so many times that it is sometimes unrealistic to give particular credit to any one person.

What we have witnessed in Figs. 15, 16 and 17 is really the development of a secondary form of geometry which would allow points to be placed into a picture by means of following a few rules and without invoking the primary geometry, which is concerned with a conical system of projectors piercing the picture plane. In Fig. 18 Marolois has reverted entirely to the use of the primary geometry. Dealing with the left half of the drawing, *abcd* is the plan of a square and O is the plan position of the observer's eye. The visual rays from the corners of the square pierce the picture plane in l, c, k and i. The distances of these points from the line mO are measured off on the front view of the picture plane, drawn separately below, as the vertical lines passing through x, y, w and v. In the side view to the right, mO represents the ground; nO is the height

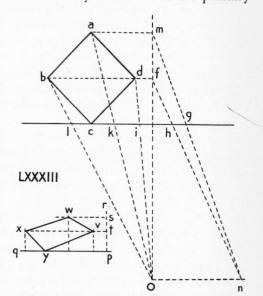

Fig. 18. Marolois's perspective projection of a square using the primary geometry concept (1629).

of the observer's eye above the ground and the visual rays fn and mn from the side view of the square pierce the picture plane in h and g. These points measured off from the line mO are transferred to the picture as the horizontal lines through tvx and sw. The intersections, of course, give the points x, y, v, w, which joined up appropriately form the picture of the square as seen from the chosen position.

More complicated projections than this, but based upon the same principle, were made, and for this it became necessary to delineate not only complex plans but rather complicated side elevations— what we would call today auxiliary views. Indeed, although most artists and geometers in these early days were concerned mainly or exclusively with the development of perspective projection, they could not help but progress the science of drawing plans, elevations and auxiliary views, since they needed these to make many of their perspective constructions. More fundamentally, they changed the concept of pictures from being just representations to that of their being projections on to planes, and as we shall see later, projection onto planes became the very foundation of descriptive geometry.

The work of Gérard Desargues was rather more than the development of perspective, in that between him and Blaise Pascal the foundations of projective geometry were laid. The ultimate development of projective geometry was in the field of mathematics, but the general ideas of this science did much for perspective. In particular, it helped to change the 'point of view' or way of looking at things mentally. In place of the imaginary lines in space—so difficult to conceive clearly—which were the basis of perspective to that time, projective geometry allowed perspective to be seen in terms of solid geometry.

There is no need for us to follow this very far, but it is of interest to have some understanding of the transformation. Desargues's Theorem stated coldly in its most uninspiring form reads thus: 'If each of two triangles has one vertex on each of three concurrent lines, then the intersections of the corresponding sides lie in a straight line, those sides being called corresponding which are opposite to vertices on the same line'. We can, however, best look at this theorem another way. Let us draw a triangle ABC as in Fig. 19 (a) and somewhere inside it mark a point D. Let us join A, B and C to D, and somewhere on AB mark a point B'. Similarly on AC and AD let us mark arbitrary points C' and D'. Now let us produce CB and $C'B'$ to meet in E, produce BD and $B'D'$ to meet in G, and CD

and $C'D'$ to meet in F. Then the theorem says that E, F and G lie on a straight line.

This is an important theory because it does not depend upon the normal Euclidean ideas. No particular angles or lengths are dealt with and it was the first of what we now call projective geometry

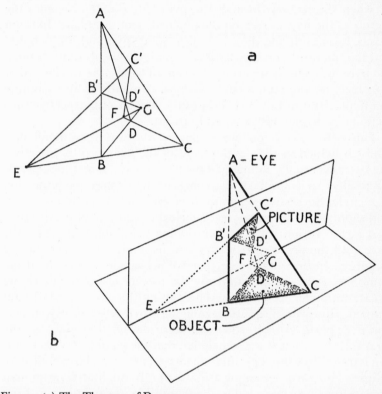

Fig. 19. (a) The Theorem of Desargues.
(b) The same lines considered as a picture of a pyramid cut by an inclined plane. If the apex is considered as the eye's position, the triangular base as the object and the inclined plane as the picture plane, then the triangle on this plane becomes the picture or projection of the object.

theorems. It can be viewed or photographed from any angle or projected onto any plane—that is, distorted—and the result remains true.

The truth of this theorem can be seen most easily by considering the lines to be those of a picture. In Fig. 19 (b) the original points *ABCD* are the picture of a pyramid on a triangular base standing on a plane. All one has to do to get Desargues's Theorem is to imagine this pyramid cut by an inclined plane as shown. Now points E, F and G must lie in a straight line, for they lie in two planes which, naturally, intersect in a straight line.

The interesting point is that this pyramid can be considered as a conical set of projectors emanating from the base BCD to the eye at A, when the section through the pyramid, $B'C'D'$, becomes the picture of the base as seen on the inclined (picture) plane. In other words, by considering the whole as a 'solid' pyramid, the 'object' and the 'picture' of it are shapes or areas, that is, sections through the pyramid. The same principles can, of course, be used whether the object be a square, a circle, or even two parallel lines running to infinity, and in this way most of the axioms of perspective projection can be demonstrated and proved.

This new way of looking at perspective was very useful but, whilst it helped in the development of the axioms of perspective, the latter eventually submerged the former with, sometimes, peculiar results. An example of this concerns the perspective projection of a circle. Successive generations of art teachers passed on more and more of the secondary geometrical techniques of perspective, that is, the various rules for positioning vanishing points and the like, until the primary geometry and its implications were nearly forgotten. In drawing the perspective projection of a circle, it became the usual practice to draw the picture of a circumscribing square into which the ellipse representing the circle would be inscribed. However, a square became distorted when drawn in perspective; parts on the further side were shorter than parts on the near side, therefore it was concluded that the picture of a circle was not a true ellipse but a peculiar distorted curve which resembled an ellipse. This idea, emerging from a purely qualitative argument spread from text-book to text-book, until it was pointed out from elementary projective geometry principles, that the picture of a circle, in general, was a section through an inclined cone on a circular base – which could be shown mathematically always to result in a true ellipse.

5

Plans and Multi-View Drawings

IN the preceding chapter we had a first glimpse of those developments which led to the depiction of solid objects through a single view exhibiting apparent shapes. The alternative approach mentioned earlier was to display such objects through a number of views each exhibiting true shapes – plans and elevations.

This alternative seems simple enough but it probably did not emerge as the result of an inspiration. Multi-view drawings undoubtedly arose in many fields quite independently and it is somewhat unrealistic to follow only one line of thought. However, for the purpose of our story we can look to one particular field to begin with – building – to see how, in theory, they might have come about.

The erection of anything – even a crude edifice such as Stonehenge – entails marking out on the ground the positions where the stones, pillars, walls, etc. are to stand. In thinking about such things, the obvious step is to make such markings to a reduced scale on some convenient flat surface – to make a plan, in fact. This, again, is simple copying; recording all the essential geometrical attributes of the real building plan, with the exception of size.

Plate 3 is of interest in this respect. In the Museum of the Louvre, Paris, are two headless statues of Gudea. Gudea was an engineer and the governor of the city-state of Lagash in the country later known as Babylon. On the knees of the statue figures the sculptor has modelled two contemporary drawing-boards. Plan views of these are shown in Plate 3. The upper one, with parts broken off, has the ground plan of a temple inscribed upon it, probably that of the temple of Ningirsu. The lower board, which is practically intact, is, however, plain. Both show some kind of scribing instrument and measuring scales. These statues are dated about 2130 B.C. and are the oldest authentic record we have of drawing equipment and measuring scales.

Possibly at one time plans were considered sufficient, the actual form of walls and so on depending upon the whim of the builder and the supply of materials and labour. This was quite general with domestic premises until even a few hundred years ago. As

37

building became more complicated and organised, the final appearance would need to be more than mere imaginings in an architect's head, and drawings would be made of particular arches, decorations and so on. Sooner or later these would be co-related to the plan and made to the same scale so that measurements could be taken off one for the other. As it became more and more necessary to complete the design before the erection of a building, so there would be a greater urge to make not only plans, but complete detailed views of the front, back and sides of buildings. This development took place in different civilisations at very different times and is so natural that it is hardly possible to determine any real point of beginning.

Plans and elevations are indeed very old in principle. We must not, however, look at these in terms of our present knowledge otherwise we get a peculiarly distorted picture. Seeing history backwards is rather different from following it forwards. Far too many persons equate plans and elevations with orthographic projection, whereas it seems very unlikely that the ancients thought of their plans as projections at all.

The front and side views of buildings and such like were essentially true shape pictures and they were often completed in later times with shadows and colour and even people incorporated. In most cases these drawings were of a size such that each view was on a different piece of parchment or paper, so that the relationship between the various views could only be determined by inspection or by captions. The development of drawing is not only a question of theory; it goes hand in hand with the development of drawing equipment. Up to the 16th and 17th centuries T-squares and drawing-boards were not in general use and many of the obvious drawing techniques we use today were quite inapplicable.

Plans were just scaled down marking out information. Architects' plans have retained this initial characteristic for obvious reasons and they are not plans in the engineering sense, that is, views from above, but ground plans.

Buildings, being static, have always, until recently, been at a more advanced state than machines, with their kinematic assemblies, and large mechanical devices were naturally developments of building practice. One reason for this was that metals did not become available in large quantities until the time of the Industrial Revolution, and the materials of construction for machines and buildings were, therefore, much the same—namely, timber and brick or stone, with small amounts of metal in the roles of clamps, bolts, axle-trees (journals for bearings) and so on.

The steam engine might be said to have triggered off the Industrial Revolution, whilst in its development it used the very materials it had helped to create in more abundance, mainly in the use of metals for cylinders, pistons, flywheels, pipes and condensers. Nevertheless the early steam engines were based upon their immediate precedents – water and wind mills and pumps – and were built integrally with the buildings which housed them. Needless to say, the drawing techniques used were also a carry-over of those used in building work. Fig. 20 is a drawing from the Boulton and Watt Collection in Birmingham dated March 21, 1792, and it is very similar indeed to many earlier drawings of water mills. The original was finished in coloured washes and the shading in the black and white rendering is meant to represent these colours. This is, of course, a 'general assembly' type of drawing and it was not intended that the cylinders, flywheel and other details should be manufactured from it. As with other building drawings, if a side view were required this would have been drawn on another sheet.*

Amédée François Frézier, an architect and military engineer, wrote a number of books, about 1738, in which we have the first direct examples of plans and elevations drawn together and projectionally related. However, the idea of plans and elevations as projections on to planes is somewhat earlier than this. As we have already seen, in the 15th and 16th centuries much attention had been paid to perspective projection, resulting in the idea of pictures being projections on to planes. As a result front and side views of buildings and other objects were regarded by some persons – mainly the more scholarly geometers – as projections on to vertical planes, and such views became known on the Continent as *ortographies*. By analogy, an object could be imagined with all its points projected onto the ground plane to give a 'view from above'. These views became known as *icnographies*.

Samuel Marolois's book on perspective, mentioned in the last chapter, started by trying to give concise definitions of the then known ways of making drawings. These were roughly as follows:

Perspective is the art which views any object through something transparent, upon which the penetrating visual rays define it.

* This drawing is included to show the bridge between buildings and machines as well as for its general interest: it is not intended to suggest that at this date it was general practice to draw views separately on different sheets.

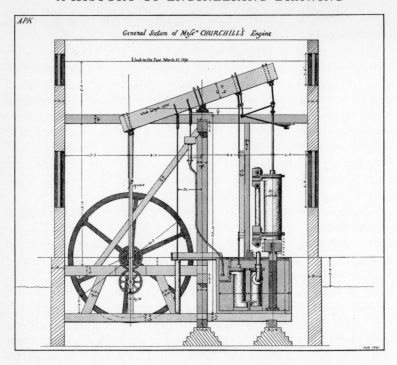

Fig. 20. A black and white copy of the original 1792 drawing in the Boulton and Watt Collection at the Birmingham City Libraries. The drawing techniques were very similar to those used for building drawings. The parts are tinted with water-colour washes and the section lining is put in freehand by brush. Basic dimensions for erection are given—not those for the manufacture of the mechanical parts which were detailed in other drawings. The '7 in square' dimension placed on the connecting rod timber is in a different hand from that of the other dimen-sioning and is probably a modification for, to scale, this timber is only about 4 in.

Scenography or *Painting* is the representation of the appearance of the object on a plane which we call the section.

Icnography is the picture on the ground plane, or the level, on which the scenographic figure is naturally standing, or thus

Icnography is the representation of the base, or plane of some body in the section when it is parallel with or equidistant from that plane.

Orthography is the picture of the front or side of a building, edifice or body, which is also called the profile, or thus

Orthography is the picture of the side of the edifice directly opposite the eye or the section, in such manner that the two surfaces, that of the sec-tion and that of the object, are parallel and equidistant to one another, which representation is also called the profile.

These definitions may not seem very clear to us especially as the terminology is rather different from that used today. Section, for instance, seems to be used as the name for the vertical plane of projection. Marolois does not make any direct distinction between projections using conical rays and those using parallel rays at right angles to the 'section'. However, the two drawings shown in Fig. 21 were attached so we can be fairly certain of what was in his mind. As we saw when dealing with perspective, the artists and

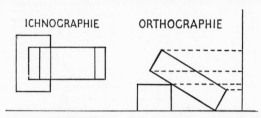

Fig. 21. Two figures from Marolois's work on perspective of 1629 illustrating his remarks on orthographic projection. 'Orthographie' was reserved for elevations, a plan being labelled 'Ichnographie'.

geometers, in developing the geometry of perspective projection, could hardly help but build up their ideas on plans and elevations at the same time, as they used the latter in order to project their perspective pictures. Fig. 22, taken from Marolois's work demonstrates the perspective projection of a cube tilted to stand on an edge. The more interested reader will find it useful to relate this drawing with Fig. 17 as the basic technique is the same. Here, however, we will restrict ourselves to noting the 'orthography' and the 'ichnography' of the cube and the way these are related one to the other by the broken line arcs. If one looks carefully one will see the front view, in effect, superimposed on the perspective view in broken lines, so that we here see quite clearly three views of an object related to one another by their positions on the paper.

Previous to this, another more famous person, Albrecht Dürer, had produced a work which demonstrated the principle of solid objects exhibited on paper through three views related to one another. Unfortunately, the subject-matter of this book was not such as to appeal very much to those persons who could benefit mostly from a systematic drawing doctrine.

Dürer is known today mainly for the beautiful engravings he has left us. The quality of these engravings is undoubtedly vested in his deep interest in shapes, and in geometry. Towards the end of his life he wrote a massive treatise on geometry, but as it was mainly a summary of what was already known, it has not assumed much importance in the eyes of historians. However, there are many interesting drawings in it; some seem to be almost copies of Alberti's on perspective; there are some elementary ideas on drawing sections through cones, and the principles of orthographic projection as such show through clearly although they are not stated as such.[27]

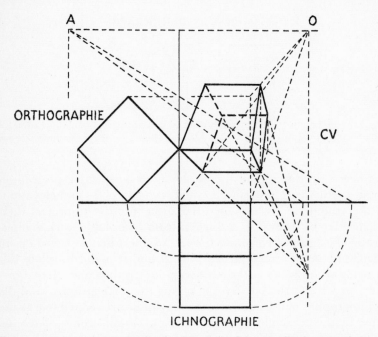

Fig. 22. A perspective projection by Marolois of a cube tilted to stand on an edge. The picture is projected from an 'Ichnographie' and an 'Orthographie', with O as the vanishing point and A as the measuring or distance point. AO is the viewing distance. The method is essentially that of Fig. 17.

Soon afterwards Dürer began writing a book on the proportions of the human figure[28] Having made many careful measurements and averaged them out, he had the task of recording them. Now, although Dürer was dealing with the human body, the problem facing him was essentially the same as that which confronted the engineer and a recognition of this at the time might have accelerated the progress of drawing practices.

Two of his drawings from this book, published in 1525, the year

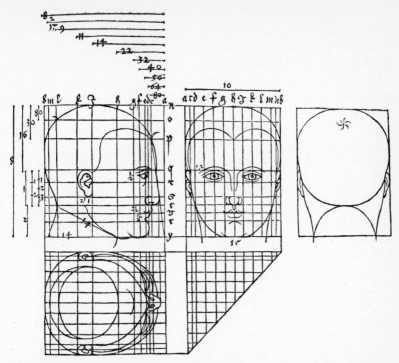

Fig. 23. (a) Dürer's systematic use of orthographic projection to define the human head and its features' proportions. Most of the dimensions given should be read as their reciprocals taking the whole man's height as unity.

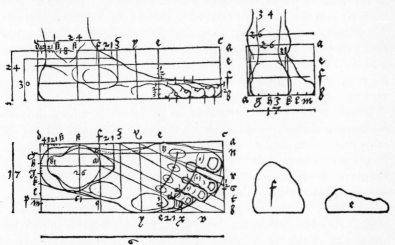

(b) A foot defined in terms of its three orthographic projections systematically arranged. Notice that Dürer arranged these in 'first angle' while his heads in (a) are in 'third angle' (see Chapter 14). The two shapes 'f' and 'e' to the right are vertical sections through the foot at *f* and *e* in the elevation and plan.

of his death, are shown in Figs. 23 and 24. These deal only with the head and feet; there were others dealing with hands and many more dealing with the whole body. These bear quite a lot of examining as they exhibit many principles familiar to us today but rather new at the time, as well as practices which may or may not have been then general.

The head is taken as 'crated' in an imaginary box which just fits it—a procedure which seems not to have become generally practised until the advent of isometric projection about 300 years later. The outlines of the head are imagined projected onto the faces of the crate, and these faces are drawn on the paper so as to be lined up in relation to one another. The relationship between these views is in many ways remarkable, although this will be better discussed in Chapter 14 (they are consistently in first or third angle). Whereas Marolois connected his plan and side views with arcs, Dürer has here used a 'mitre' line; the interesting point to note is that it slopes the opposite way to what one would expect. The lines in plan and side view (side view is used here in the modern conventional sense and is actually the front of the face) connect up properly, but only because the human face is symmetrical; if this had been an unsymmetrical body the plan would have become a mirror image, that is reversed top to bottom.

In passing, the dimensioning is of some interest. The arrowheads at the ends of dimension lines are back to front compared with modern practice, the flats instead of the points denoting the ends. The figures on these lines may also appear strange because the smaller lengths have on them the larger figures. These figures represent their reciprocals; the height of a man was taken as unity, and the head as 1/8th high and long, and 1/10th broad, shown as 8 and 10 respectively.

Dürer developed his orthographic projection methods through their natural stages. Fig. 24 shows the next stage; the face of the crate containing the head's profile is drawn tilted and lines are projected across to give the new view of the head, the horizontal distances in this new view (that is, the vertical lines) being obtained from a full face view of the head as in Fig. 23 (a).

The term 'projected' has been used above and, as this is used slightly differently than hitherto, we had better be clear upon what we mean. When we speak of projection in its most fundamental sense, we mean lines in space running from points on an object to the picture plane or plane of projection. If we consider Fig. 23 (a) again, ignoring the head and concentrating upon the crate itself, this is represented as a number of rectangles. We can look upon the arrangement of these simply as a drawing convenience, that is, the plan is positioned below the front view of the crate (containing the profile of the head) so that its length may be determined simply by dropping the left and right edges of the upper rectangle down to the lower one. In this way we do not have to measure the length in the front view and again measure it in the plan view, and, of course,

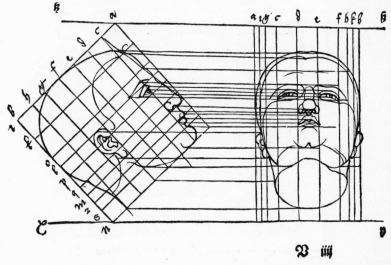

Fig. 24. A demonstration of projectional technique by Dürer to give an auxiliary view. The vertical lines in the auxiliary view are taken from a front face view similar to that in Fig. 23 (a). The next logical step is illustrated in Fig. 56.

similarly with the front and side views. The lines connecting these views are almost universally today termed 'projectors' and we shall therefore use this term from henceforth. In examining old drawings we should not, however, jump to the conclusion that a drawing exhibiting projectors of this sort demonstrates that the draughtsman was conversant with the true principles of orthographic projection. As time went by most craftsmen grasped the essential idea of plans and elevations, if only through usage, although most were unfamiliar with the concept of projection—just as many quite young children recognise the truths shown in plans and elevations without any knowledge of the theory of projection. The separation of plans and elevations, and true shape drawings in general, from the idea of projection onto planes is very important and has had repercussions which are still with us today.

Whilst multi-view drawings took on a much more methodical character when considered in terms of projection onto planes, many educators still believe such principles to be redundant and the simple 'picture concept' has in recent years been re-introduced into certain American books as an adequate yet more natural alter-

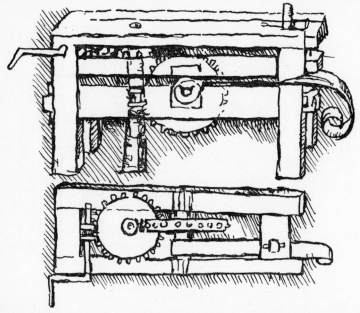

Fig. 25. Sketches of a rolling mill for forming lead and copper strips by Leonardo da Vinci. Notice that whilst front and top views are given, these are essentially 'pictures'.

native approach. The idea of plans and elevations being not just true shape drawings, but projections onto planes, was finally systematised and promulgated by Gaspard Monge in 1795 and, in due course, we shall see how this came about.

Whilst Dürer, and later some architects, demonstrated the general axioms of orthographic projection resulting in a number of projectionally related views, there is little evidence to suggest that these were used by practical persons, especially with respect to mechanical devices. In the Middle Ages, buildings and ships had reached a high state of development and the architect and ship-wright were professional people. What machines did exist, were, however, crude and the work of inspired craftsmen. Progress was slow because of the lack of mechanical theory and the hand methods of construction. One does not find drawings of machines from this period comparable with contemporary building and ship drawings.

It is interesting to note that even when an all-round genius, such as Leonardo da Vinci (1452–1519), thought on paper about machines, he nearly always did so in terms of apparent view pictures, and not in terms of true plans and elevations. Fig. 25, exhibiting the general layout of a rolling mill using a series of worm and worm-wheel drives, is fundamentally an elevation with a related plan, but Leonardo could not help turning both into 'pictures' by giving each view the additional 'depth' dimension.

6

Constructional Drawings: Sun-Dialling and Stone-Cutting

THE development of drawing dealt with up to this point has all been concerned with the representation of objects. Drawings are, however, often used for other purposes and, in particular, for deriving information which is inherent in the object represented but not immediately accessible. For instance, a cone may be easily represented by a circle for its plan view and a triangle for its front view; if, however, we need to make such a cone from a piece of sheet metal or paper we have to make another drawing—a development of the surface. We want a shape which is implied in the representational drawings but is not given.

This is, of course, just a special example of the use of drawings to calculate particular shapes, which are necessary to make things, from other data. In this chapter we are going to trace technical drawing from another source, through the art of sun-dialling and stone-cutting—two very odd subjects, it may seem.

First of all, let us look at a few geometrical ideas. The drawing of a triangle and the cutting out of a triangle from a sheet of card are, geometrically speaking, the same. Likewise, drawing a circle and making a disc or wheel are the same in character. It is true that the wheel, being a 'thing', is more useful than its representation on paper, but from the geometrical point of view there is no distinction. To draw the circle one uses a pencil in a pair of compasses. To make a disc one substitutes a cutting edge for the pencil. If we must make a distinction we can call the drawing 'graphical geometry' and the physical counterpart 'constructional geometry'.

Now, so long as man was dealing with plane geometrical shapes he had no difficulty in thinking about them, representing them or making them. Both the drawing and the thing were geometrically the same except that the thing had thickness whilst the drawing in theory had none. The first real difficulties arose when man had to consider three-dimensional *problems* rather than simple

48

PLATE 3

long o^m 29

long o^m 32

Representations of two drawing-boards from statues of Gudea of Ur in The Museum of the Louvre, Paris. The upper board displays the ground plan of a Ziggurat and both have representations of a scribing instrument and a scale. The statues are dated *c*. 2130 B.C. From *Découvertes en Chaldée*.

A water-colour drawing of a Shipwright's Drawing Office from Matthew Baker's Manuscript of about 1586. The drawing has been made in an empirical form of perspective. The representation of the drawing on the table has not been rendered in perspective probably because the artist wished the viewer to see the true nature of the ship 'draught' being laid out.

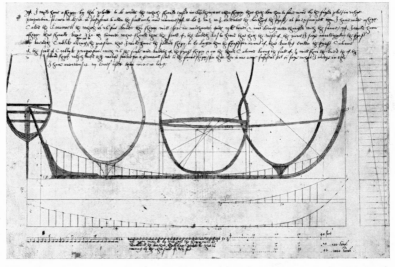

A Ship Draught from Matthew Baker's Manuscript of about 1586. This work was in the nature of a text-book and this drawing, whilst instructive of the methods in use, is not as a whole typical of complete Ship Draughts of this period. The wording above, though in English, is written in an old, now unfamiliar script. It states that weight and capacity are proportional to the cube of linear measurements and that this same Draught can be used for ships of different tonnage by using appropriate scales. Various scales are given below.

three-dimensional *things*,* problems he found difficult to represent let alone solve in terms of ordinary plane geometry. The immediate methods of solving such problems meant throwing over graphical techniques and using constructional ones. Constructions are, of course, solid things and not drawings, but from these constructional solutions, graphical techniques emerged.

Sun-dialling is a useful subject with which to demonstrate these methods and, later in this chapter, we shall see a three-dimensional problem solved by a three-dimensional construction. In the meantime we can see how drawing, in a sense, became mixed up with the making of the actual hardware. There is nothing strange in this, of course, for today we mark out jobs on metal or wood before we commence fashioning.

In order to understand the problems we must find out what was entailed in the art of sun-dialling.

How many of us if left in some remote part of the world, unaware of our location and without a compass or watch, could construct a sun-dial which would give reasonably accurate time throughout the year? Probably few, for all our education; yet this is the problem which faced our forefathers; of course even in the earlier civilisations there were forms of water clock, but these had to be set and calibrated with something more ultimate, and the only 'natural clock' that could be used was the spinning of the earth on its axis. Any other timing device had to be related to this. It is probably true that the way of life then did not demand very accurate timekeeping, but mankind being what it is, the subject was pursued for its intellectual challenge far in advance of requirements for practical purposes, and long after astronomy and good mechanical clocks had made it redundant. At a later date much the same could be said about the development of perspective projection which has fascinated geometrically minded persons right through to today.

If we erect an upright post, the position of its shadow will denote the passing of time. However, the shadow does not move through angles equal to those through which the sun appears to pass. If one had some other way of reckoning hours – which in ancient times one had not – after each hour the shadow's position could be marked, and the next day one could tell the time by observing the position of the shadow with respect to the markings. However, these markings would appertain strictly only to the day on which they were

* Such as a box or room which is really a collection of simple planes having a simple relationship with one another.

made, for, through the year the sun's path varies, reaching a high point in summer and a low point in winter. This not only affects the lengths of the shadows cast, but also the relationship between the angles through which the sun appears to move and the angles the shadow passes through. In all, this is a very nice problem in three-dimensional geometry.

Although a great deal of astronomical knowledge was available to the ancients, this problem was not properly solved in Europe until about the 16th century. Sun-dials of a sort had been made for a thousand years before this date and, in the 1st century B.C. Vitruvius [47] gave instructions for making a sun-dial using the Analemma construction and mentioned a number of others. But time then had not the same meaning as today, and the day was the period between sunrise and sunset. This variable period, divided into 12 'hours', meant that the 'hours' were not of constant duration throughout the day or from day to day during the year. Whilst the methods to be described were built upon the ancient writings, they were conceived in an age when an hour was always equal to a twenty-fourth part of the day. If we consider the post above to be erected at one of the earth's poles, then it lies in the axis of the earth's spin. Many of the ancients considered the earth stationary with the sun moving round it embedded in a celestial sphere; this viewpoint makes very little difference, except that accounting for the seasons raises complications. With the post lying in the earth's axis, the shadow of the post would then pass through angles exactly equal to the apparent motion of the sun; so to make a sun clock one would only need to draw a circle about the post as centre and divide it into 24 parts. Since the sun's rays may be considered as being parallel, such conditions could be reconstructed anywhere on earth by erecting a post so that it lay in a line parallel to the earth's axis; a disc placed on the post like a wheel on an axle could then be divided into 24 parts just as the ground plane would be at the poles.

Such a sun-dial had certain limitations. Just as the poles have alternately six months of daylight and six months of darkness, so the shadow cast by the post would be on one side of the disc for half of the year and on the other side for the other half–and during the change-over period the shadow would be vague or non-existent on either side. It was consequently considered more practical to project the lines from the disc onto some other surface, usually a horizontal or vertical one.

The sun-dialling problem provided, therefore, two separate problems. One of these was finding the angle at which to erect a post (or the angle to make the edge of a triangle) so that it was parallel to the earth's axis. The other was the projection of the 24-hour lines from the theoretical disc onto the horizontal plane – indeed, once the basic problem was solved, those interested in the theory developed it in all manner of ways. Some of these are briefly recorded in the title – virtually synopsis – of a 17th-century book:

THE ART OF DYALLING
in Two Parts

The first shewing plainly, and in a manner mechanically how to make dyals to all plaines, either Horizontall, Murall, declining, reclining or inclining, with the theoricke of the Arte.

The second how to performe the selfe same in a more artificiall kinde and without the use of Arithmeticke, together with concave and convex dyalls, and the inserting of the 12 lignes and the howers of any country in any dyall, with many other things to the same Art appertaining. The whole differing much from all that hath beene heretofore written of the same Art by any other, and the greater part wrought by diverse new conceits of the author, never yet extant, now published by John Blagrave, of Reading, Gentleman and Mathematician, this year 1609

We will deal with the two parts of the sun-dialling problem in the reverse order for convenience.

Let us, given the equally-spaced hour lines on the disc or plane at right angles to the post, or style as it was called, see how these were projected onto another plane to give unequally spaced lines. The general method is recorded in John Blagrave's book mentioned above and this is quoted below so that one may see exactly how such instructions were given in a 17th-century book. To avoid confusion it is worth remembering that to Blagrave the horizontal or reference plane was the plane through the equator or the horizontal plane at the poles. For this reason he refers to the horizontal plane at the place where the sun-dial is being made as the oblique plane. An inclining plane is what we would call oblique, that is between our horizontal and vertical planes, while an axtree is a corruption of axle-tree used in a theoretical sense to mean an axis (see Fig. 26).

A Dyall is nothing else but the description of 24 hower-lines which the Sunne by his diurnall revolution projecteth by the shade of a visible axtree line lying parallel to the invisible axtree of the world, on some visible plaine or other that lieth parallell to the invisible plaine of some great cyrcle of the heavens or other. And because the Equinoctiall cyrcle

. . . is the only great circle of the sphere that is described by the same diurnal revolution; therefore out of him, as from a roote, is derived the projectment of these 24 hower-lines on any other great circle or plaine whatsoever; for Example.*

Let AD be any oblique Horizontall plaine, admit levell with our Horizon cyrcle here at Reading. Let his one side AB serve for the Base line and square to it draw the Meridian line EF. Then let there stand on the Base line AB two other plaines, the one a murall plaine as BK perpendicular erected on the Horizontal plaine AD, the other BM an inclining plaine elevated above it, so much as the Equinoctials height with us cometh unto, which is 38 degrees, 25 minutes. . . . Then thrust a pinne, style or wyer of infinite length through some point as H of that Equinoctiall plaine BM chosen directly over the Meridian EF so that the same pinne stand square to BM, so shall it of necessity lye in the axtree of the world, and withall broach through the Horizontal plaine AD at C and the murall plaine BK at I. Then draw the lines HE and IE both perpendicular to AB. And so are IE and HE and CE become the 12 of clock hower-lines to those 3 plaines, those lines lying all three in the plaine of the Meridian cyrcle of our Horizon, and IEC and IHE and CHE are three rectangle triangles. Then on I, H and C describe 3 circles or rather here 3 semicircles all touching at the point E of AEB, viz KES in the murall plaine BK, and TEV in the Equinoctial plaine MB, and WEX in our Horizontall plaine AD. So shall AB be touch-line to all 3 cyrcles, which you shall extend either way to P and Q. Then divide the semicircle TEV of the Equinoctiall plaine, called therefore for this respect the Equinoctiall circle (though indeed it be the circle of the Polar dyalls) into 12 equal parts, viz 6 on each side of E. Then from H extend lines through every of these 12 parts, till they crosse the touch-line PQ as you see HE, HN, HL, etc. for those are the very hower-lines that the shade of the axtree IHC maketh by the Sunnes diurnall revolution about the earth, as aforesayd, on the Equinoctial or Polar plaine MB manifesting also the Theoricke of the Polar diall; for indeed the Polar Horizon is of some called Horizon obliquissimus.

Lastly, from I and C extend lines unto all those crossing at N, L, P, etc. and those shall furnish you with hower-lines for both the other dials, as you see. The reason is because the hower-lines projected by the selfe same shade of the axtree IHC on the murall plaine KB and the Horizontall plaine AD must of necessity crosse all at the touch-line PQ because the line PQ lieth in every one of their plaines, and is the common section of those three great circles of the sphere, which these three plaines represent, that is to say, they do all three crosse one another on that line PQ.[9]

The idea of lines projectionally related to one another meeting at the intersection of the planes containing them is fundamental

* The full meaning of this will become apparent when Figs. 29 and 30 are discussed.

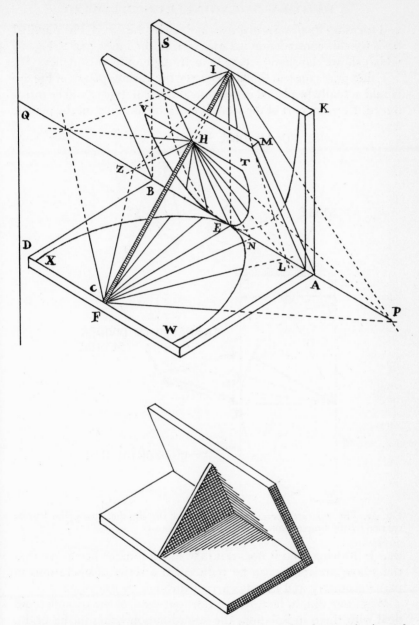

Fig. 26. Basis for the projection of the hour lines from a polar plane to a horizontal or vertical plane to make a sun-dial, from Blagrave's *The Art of Dyalling in Two Parts*, 1609. The shadows in the lower sketch (not in the original) give the physical basis for the above projection.

and turns up in all sorts of guises in drawing history.* The physical basis for this construction is easily seen in the lower half of Fig. 26 which shows the shadow cast by a triangle onto two planes.

Using pure constructional geometry the various planes of Fig. 26 would actually be placed in position and a real style would be introduced. Even so, part of the work is marking out lines on the planes,

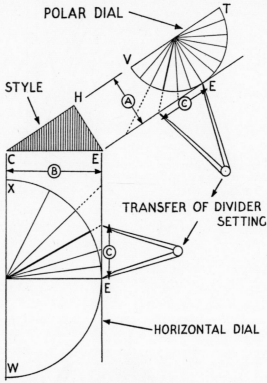

POLAR DIAL

STYLE

TRANSFER OF DIVIDER SETTING

HORIZONTAL DIAL

Fig. 27. The separate operations which allow the sun-dial 'projection' to be carried out by simple plane geometry constructions.

that is drawing, and it does not take much intelligence to see that the whole projection can be reduced to a series of operations in plane geometry and largely carried through by drawing.

What one did, in fact, was to take out some of the triangles and deal with them in isolation, the co-ordination being in the brain. One could draw, for example, the triangle *HCE* in Fig. 27 since angle *HCE* was known. Assuming a suitable scale, this gives (A)

* See, for instance, Desargues's Theorem, page 35.

and (B), the radii of the two semicircles *TEV* and *WEX*, so that the latter could be drawn separately, the first on paper or some convenient surface and the second possibly on the sun-dial itself, or on paper, the angles found being subsequently transferred to the sun-dial. Any one of the equally spaced hour-lines on the first circle could be produced to give dimension (C) which could then be transferred to a similar line for the other circle. When this had been done for all the lines, the hour-lines were successfully transferred or, figuratively speaking, projected upon the new reference plane, and only plane geometry and common sense had been used.

This method in practice is shown in Fig. 28 – a picture taken from a book of 1643 by Abraham Bosse, although the theories and methods expounded are those of Gérard Desargues.[12] This illustrates the actual transference of lengths by using dividers. Notice that the top part is graphical, that is, drawn, and the bottom part constructional, that is, made up from materials. The hour-lines are marked temporarily here by stretched cords, although geometrically speakng a stretched thread is as much a line as one drawn on a surface.

In Blagrave's method, he has assumed that one knows where one is situated and therefore knows the angle of latitude. The figures given in the quotation are, indeed, the complement of the angle of latitude at Reading, England. He has also assumed that one can determine the direction of North, both these pieces of information being required to place a style parallel to the axis of the earth's spin. Even if one did not have this information, it would not be very difficult to locate the Pole Star and measure the required angle. However, this whole sun-dialling problem became one of intellectual interest to mathematicians and geometers and many of these, looking at it purely as a theoretical problem, invented all sorts of geometrical techniques which may or may not have found practical application. As exercises in solid or three-dimensional geometry they are of considerable interest, partly because they played a part in subsequent developments and partly because they demonstrate a state in which such problems were solved through a mixture of graphical and constructional techniques.

Gérard Desargues – an engineer, architect, mathematician and geometer, who lived 1593 to 1662 and whose projective geometry theory we met in the chapter on perspective – tackled the problem of how to raise a post, or rod, parallel to the earth's axis assuming one had no information to work upon, and he produced what he

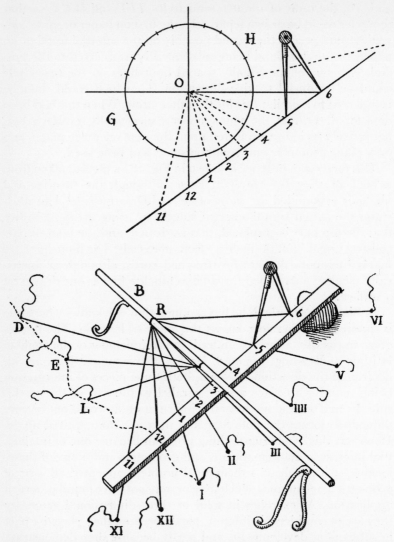

Fig. 28. The sun-dial projection carried out with the aid of threads, from Bosse's *La Manière universelle de M. Desargues pour poser l'essieu, etc. aux cadrans au soleil,* 1643.

called his Universal Method. What is to be described, then, would be a preliminary to the type of projection displayed above.

In Desargues's method one takes a point *B* some way above the ground. In Fig. 29 it is the end of a rod supported at *A*. As the sun

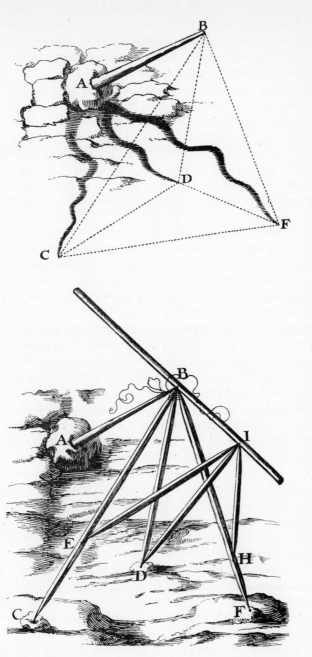

Fig. 29. Positioning the style of a sun-dial, from Bosse's work of 1643.

moves round, the shadow of this rod will also move. At three different times in the day, mark the end of the shadow to give three points *C*, *D* and *F*. *BC*, *BD* and *BF* represent the paths of the sun's rays at those times, as shown in the upper engraving.

Now comes the intriguing part. One constructs three rods to take the place of these rays, and these are shown in the bottom picture. The shortest length *BD* is measured off from *B* down the other rods to give points *E* and *H*. Three more rods are now prepared; these must be equal in length, but differing in length from *BD*. They are fixed in some manner at points *D*, *E* and *H* and the other ends manœuvred until they all meet at one point, *I*. If a rod is now fixed through points *B* and *I*, this rod lies parallel to the earth's axis.

This is an interesting example of the use of constructional geometry in the solution of a three-dimensional problem. There were probably similar constructions for similar types of problems. However well these seemed in theory, there is no doubt that any real accuracy could hardly be expected and inadequacy was one of the spurs towards better methods.

Perhaps the most interesting question at the moment is simply why this peculiar construction should work. The answer is a little difficult to see from Bosse's illustration as this is somewhat distorted from the truth. We saw earlier that if one erected a post at the North Pole the earth would virtually spin round it, from which it follows that the shadow would be of the same length at any hour. In consequence, the distance from the tip of the post to the tip of the shadow would remain constant, as shown in Fig. 30 (a). By making *BE* and *BH* equal to *BD*, the Polar conditions are reconstructed, and *D*, *E* and *H* lie in a plane parallel to the horizontal at the poles, as in Fig. 30 (b). *BI* then, must be at right angles to this plane; but since, in the construction of Fig. 29 there is no real plane—only three points—it is impractical to use a square against it. So a simple alternative is resorted to. In Fig. 30 (c), the triangles *BEX*, *BDX* and *BHX* are identical, with *BE*, *BD* and *BH* equal in length. If some arbitrary point, *I*, is selected on the post, triangles *IEX*, *IDX* and *IHX* are identical, with *IE*, *ID* and *IH* equal in length. Working the other way around, as in Fig. 29 with rods of equal length attached to points on the first rods equidistant from *B*, *B* and *I* must lie in a line parallel to the earth's axis.

The fixing of the rods *IE*, *ID* and *IH* in Fig. 29 was somewhat impractical, so Desargues developed his basic method to make the physical construction more simple. Instead of six rods as before, only three were required as shown in Fig. 31. These were placed with one end of each on the points of the shadow (determined as in Fig. 29) and the other ends were manœuvred to meet in point *I*, *BI* again being the axis required. These rods were not, however, of some arbitrary length as in the last case, but their lengths had to be individually determined for any set of conditions. Desargues worked

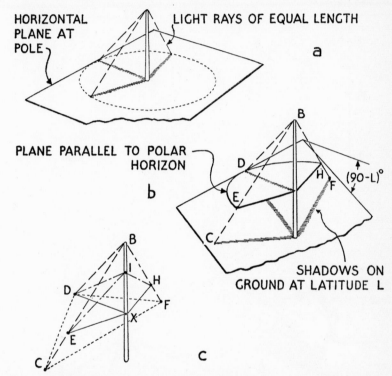

HORIZONTAL PLANE AT POLE

LIGHT RAYS OF EQUAL LENGTH

a

PLANE PARALLEL TO POLAR HORIZON

b

B

D

H

E

F

C

(90-L)°

SHADOWS ON GROUND AT LATITUDE L

B

I

D

H

E

X

F

C

c

Fig. 30. Demonstrating the geometrical basis of the construction given in Fig. 29.

out a graphical construction for determining these lengths, and we now have the rather extraordinary situation in which a very complex graphical construction was embarked upon, not to give one immediately the answer, but to provide information towards building up a piece of constructional geometry, which in turn would provide the answer.

Whilst the constructional drawing Desargues provided is difficult to follow, this is mainly due to the large number of successive steps

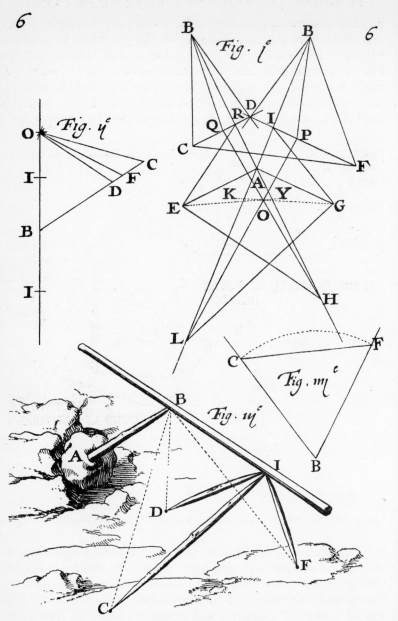

Fig. 31. A graphical construction devised by Desargues to make the material construction more simple, from Bosse's work of 1643.

taken. In principle, like the projection of the hour-lines on a dial, the method depended solely upon isolating a number of triangles; some were given at the start, and the others were derived. Instead of drawing these triangles separately, Desargues showed them by revolving each into the ground plane, that is, into the plane of drawing.

This technique is better followed in a more simple example from a different field—stone-cutting. We have little knowledge of the early methods used by stone-cutters; they belonged to Guilds and were extremely secretive over all matters concerning their trade,

Fig. 32. Part of a plate from Diderot's *Encyclopedia* showing a stone-cutter marking out his stone with rule, square and compasses. From Vol. 1, Architecture, Maçonnerie, Plate I.

whilst few probably were literate enough to record their techniques. However, a number of books appeared in the 17th century—mostly French or translations from the French—written by more academic men on what many called 'the secrets of architecture'. These books were not really a recording of stone-cutting geometrical constructions, but rather expositions by the various authors displaying their own rational methods. However, there was probably little difference between the two as far as results were concerned. Empiricists have always tended to find methods which gave the correct result even if they did not always understand why.

Desargues, again, wrote a great deal on the geometry of stone-cutting practice and his friend Bosse, as with much of Desargues's work, put this together into books. [13] Fig. 33 is based on an illustration from one of these books published in 1663. The top left drawing illustrates some typical stone shapes in masonry, although many more complex shapes were often encountered. The right upper drawing gives a typical stone with bevels and squares placed on the various angles. In order that this exposition should be clear, this illustration has been altered from the original to fit in with the geometrical construction shown below which pertains to it. The stone is basically a rectangular prism, except that it has the front face inclined to the vertical–'battered'–and has the left vertical face cut across obliquely. Angle GBH is a primary one as is angle NAP, and both may be marked directly upon the stone. Angle LAN, however, is a compound angle formed by the intersection of two inclined planes, as is angle EAP.

The stone can, of course, be cut without pre-determining these angles; suppose however another stone is to be cut to abut on to the left face, one either has to wait until the first stone is actually cut so that angle LAN can be measured, or one can work out this angle so that both stones can be cut simultaneously and then fitted together. Writing about this drawing, Bosse says:

And there are two methods; one is to apply the bevels and a set square to the actual stone as is represented in the top figure and of which I shall give no particulars.

The other is to find out with the bevels and set square the shapes of the panels, and to do this, in the figure below, draw with a ruler a line PAB; put to the length of the line, for example at A, one of the edges of the bevel set to the angle between the levelled front face and course and draw along the other leg a straight line AN.

Take on this line AN another point, for example N, and from that point lead across line AB a line NBH perpendicular to AB.

Put the corner of the bevel, set to the angle between the front face and the level HBG, to the point B with one of the legs beyond the line AB, along the line BH and draw along the edge of the other leg a line BG.

Draw from point N up to the line BG a line NG parallel to line AB. Take from point N a line NL perpendicular to line AN.

Open the compass from B to G, then by turning on the point B, go with the other point to give E on the line HBN to give the line AE.

Open the compass from N to G, then by turning on the point N, go with the other point to L on the line NL, to give the line AL.

The angle BAE is that of the front face panel. The angle NAL is that of the oblique side.* And if you have been precise in the operation, the lines AL and AE are equal to one another.

* Actually the supplement of angle NAL in the block's picture.

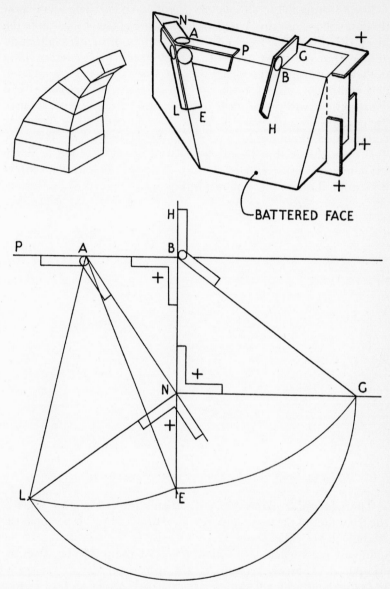

Fig. 33. A stone-cutter's graphical construction for determining compound angles, from Bosse's *La Pratique du trait à preuves de M. Desargues Lyonnois, pour la coupe de pierres en l'architecture*, 1663.

Bosse goes on to say, in a rather complicated way, that the reader should not assume from this simple first example–in which the block could be cut quite well without determining the compound angles–that the construction is not necessary, for in determining the set of voussoirs–the wedge-shaped stones which form an arch or a vault roof–amongst other occasions, some of the geometrical constructions will prove to be indispensable. And, indeed, some of the constructions in these old books on stone-cutting are extremely complicated, the more so as no rational explanations are given.

It seems likely that Desargues arrived at this solution in much the same way as he tackled the sun-dialling problem. The three-dimensional reasoning is shown in Fig. 34.

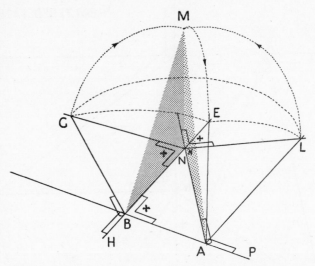

Fig. 34. Demonstrating the triangles revolved flat in Fig. 33.

The triangular plane MBN represents the 'batter' or slope of the front face of the stone and, revolved about BN, this becomes the triangle BNG. The plane MAN likewise is the true shape of the obliquely cut vertical face which, revolved about AN, becomes the triangle ANL. Since NG and NL are, in reality, MN they must be the same length, hence the arc about centre N joining G to L. In a similar way the triangle ABM can be laid down to become triangle ABE; BE and BG are then really BM and so are of the same length, and so on.

The shortcoming of the methods we have seen above is that they led to problem solving by rote. It seems fairly obvious that Desargues had himself worked out a number of generalised drawing doctrines and, by using these, he could produce solutions to most of the then current constructional problems–which were mainly concerned with stone-cutting and carpentry. However, only the final solutions got published, not the generalisations which lay behind them.

There was a second restriction inherent in these kinds of construction. They dealt only with angles and it made no difference what size one made the geometrical construction. This gave the whole an air of abstraction, when the various lines could otherwise have been scaled from the stone block; the various triangles would then have been truly representations of the block's panels and not just lines to give angles. To put it another way–in the earlier chapters of this book we considered the development of drawing in the purely representational sense; here we are dealing with drawing in the constructional sense, to derive information from that which is given. The two really needed combining and, although Desargues came very near to it, we have to wait for Monge's *Descriptive Geometry* before we see this comprehensively accomplished.

When we come to discuss Monge we shall see that he was vehemently opposed to the empirical constructions taught under the heading of carpentry drawing. Once again, however, there is little direct evidence recorded for us to judge the worth of the drawing methods used in carpentry, as wood-workers were just as secretive as stone-cutters. Shipwrights, it seems, were the exceptions, probably because being virtually ship designers they were more highly educated, and we give below instructions as recorded in William Sutherland's *The Shipbuilder's Assistant* of 1711 (see Fig. 35).

Figure A is a Pair of winding Stairs, having a Nuel in the Center, and a Side or String for the Circumference. The Portal or Clear of the Scuttle, A, B, C, D, being pointed down on the lower Plane where the Stairs stand, and a Right Square being made as in the Figure, with a Pair of Compasses or other Instrument for that Purpose, describe the Arch A, D, placing one Point of the Instrument in C. Make a streight Line A, F, D. Then observing the perpendicular Height between Decks, divide that Number into as many equal parts as you please, for a Compliment of Steps; taking notice that 10 or 11 Inches ought to be the greatest Distance between Step and Step. Then divide the Circle A, D, into as many Divisions as you allow to have Steps, as a, b, c, d, e, f, and sweeping the Arch K, L, from the same Center, divide it into the same number of equal Parts as you did the Arch A, D, first observing to set off the Round of the Lower Step from the Line C, D, to L, so that the Rise be under the upper

Plane. Then with an Elliptis or Spiral Mould . . . mark out all the Steps and Rises, by running the Mould backward and forward. Then proceed to find the extream Length of the Side. And in order thereto, take the Perpendicular Height from the upper Edge of one Deck's Plank

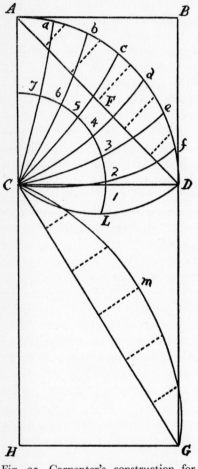

to the upper Edge of the other, and set off from D to G, and from C to H. Prolong the Bigness of the Scuttle to G, H, then draw the Diagonal Line C, G, which is the extream Length of the String or Side. Then Dividing the Line A, D, into any Number of equal Parts as the prick'd Lines, being perpendicular from A, D, divide also the Line C, G, into as many equal Parts, and draw perpendicular Lines as in the other Part. Transfer the Heights of the Sweep A, D, to C, G, and find a radius to sweep C, m, G, accordingly, which is the true Rounding of the String or Side in the extream Length.[68]

The first part of the above is straight forward enough and refers to the laying out of a plan of the stairs, that is, their projection onto the deck plane. Be it noted that this probably meant drawing the projection on the deck itself as much as on paper. The second part is not at all clear, although it appears to be a geometrical construction to find the true length of the outer edge of the stairs—which is a helix. The rational way to do this is to develop the cylindrical surface enveloping the stairs, upon which development the helix will appear as a diagonal line. The method given above, if this was the intention, is irrational. An approximation would result if GH were made equal to the length AD, for CG would then represent the true

Fig. 35. Carpenter's construction for laying out a set of spiral stairs between the decks of a ship, from Sutherland's *The Shipbuilder's Assistant* of 1711.

length of the diagonal through a rectangular prism. As it is, *CmG* is considerably short of the true helix length.

Whether the reasoning in the above quotation is typical of its time or not, the quotation itself is useful in giving some idea of the methods used by shipwrights, millwrights and so on before the start of the modern era of engineering.

Before we finish this chapter, let us look once again at Fig. 19 in the section on perspective and Fig. 29 in this chapter. Both are from Desargues – one deals with his theorem about projective geometry and the other with sun-dialling. Both figures can be regarded as pyramids on triangular bases with an oblique cutting plane through them. It seems quite apparent that Desargues's studies in the one direction fertilised his ideas in another, as is often the case.

Stone-cutting, sun-dialling and carpentry are most rewarding fields of study for those interested in the early stages of technical drawing. They have been rather neglected in modern times because, in studying drawing, there is a tendency to concentrate upon what is marked on pieces of paper, and to forget that much of what today we would call detail drawing was marked on the actual stone or wood in the past instead of on paper.

7

Ship sand Forts : Water-Lines and Figured Plans

WHILST man was endeavouring on the one hand to find ways of representing on paper three-dimensional forms based on simple geometrical solids–cubes, pyramids and the like–and on the other hand to find ways of solving problems in three-dimensional geometry, he quite unconsciously started out on another track which was to lead to methods of representing 'streamlined' shapes and bodies of irregular form–those which had no edges to represent as lines.

We can follow this most conveniently by commencing with ship draughting. Plate 4 shows a shipwright's drawing office of the 16th century, with a shipwright at work on a ship draught.* This picture comes from Matthew Baker's Manuscript housed in the Pepysian Library at Cambridge, England. Plate 5 is another drawing from this manuscript showing in more detail the layout of a ship. It depicts the keel, stem and stern, and, revolved through a right angle, some of the rib shapes. The revolving of these shapes into the plane of the paper has much in common with those pictures in earlier chapters which showed wheels and so on similarly depicted. Revolving shapes so that they can be represented as the true shapes we know them to be, is a natural, instinctive action carried out, as we have seen, even by very young children who have no formal knowledge of drawing–yet basically it is the same as the techniques used by Desargues in the last chapter, although his revolving of triangles into the plane of the paper was a little more systematic.

This manuscript was in many respects the equivalent of a textbook and, in looking at Plate 5, we must not jump to the conclusion that this is how ship draughts looked in the 16th century. In fact, the shapes for the ribs were generally drawn separately and not superimposed on the side view. For convenience we will use the simple terms side view, front view and plan, although in ship-draughting terminology they were called respectively the sheer-

---

* 'Ship draught' was, and is, used to refer to a ship drawing.

plan, draught or plan of elevation; the body-plan or plan of projection; and the half-breadth or floor plan.

The shapes of the ribs in this Plate may seem somewhat arbitrary at first sight, but they were, nevertheless, drawn carefully by compasses on a complex series of centres. The curves drawn in such a ship draught had to be reproduced full size on the lofting floor so that the actual ribs could be constructed. Now in these times the only curve which could be simply defined, and therefore reproduced, was the arc of a circle. In consequence, there are on the rib section at the centre of this drawing a number of centres marked for the various arcs. Rib sections for the whole ship had to be defined in this way and this was accomplished by determining all the arcs and radii.

Whilst ships got bigger, the technique of shipbuilding remained remarkably constant for many hundreds of years. Drawing techniques, however, steadily improved, and a typical ship draught of about 1670 is shown in Plate 7. Whilst this has much of interest in many directions, we are concerned only with certain drawing aspects. Notice that the drawing of the rib sections has now become simplified into merely defining the outside curves. These were superimposed upon one another as shown in the lower right part of the illustration. Since the ribs were symmetrical about the vertical centre line only half of each section was drawn, those from the stern to amidships commonly on the left and those from the bow to amidships on the right. This convention is still generally adhered to today.

The 'half-breadths' can be seen quite clearly as horizontal lines at the points of greatest breadth of each section. These half-breadths were stepped off with dividers and laid off on the plan to give the half-breadth plan. It was common also to mark off in the side view, or sheer plan, the 'height of breadth' lines, found by stepping off with dividers the heights from the front view of the rib sections. Very often proportional dividers were used in this drawing operation, so that the rib-sections could be drawn to a much larger scale than the plan and side views.

In architectural or building drawings the technique of transferring dimensions from the ground plan to other views by dividers was quite normal. In ship draughting this process became the most important and time-consuming part of the drawing.

Another curve which could be plotted in the plan was the waterline. Assuming that this was parallel to the keel, it could be represented in the front view showing the rib sections by drawing a horizontal line at the requisite height above the keel. This line would naturally cut all the rib sections and, by transferring the various horizontal widths from each rib section to the appropriate place in the plan, a plan of the water-line shape of the ship could be developed. Shipwrights, even in the days of the early wooden walls, had enough empirical knowledge to be able to predict fairly well the depth to which the hull of a ship would sink when the ship was empty, partially laden and fully loaded. This, of course, allowed them to plot three water-lines.

Now this is of considerable significance. In time it became apparent that there was no need to adhere to real water-lines. One could postulate theoretical water-lines at any height up the ship's hull, and the sum total of a large number of water-lines adequately defined the ship's form. The rib sections in the front view could, of course, be looked at in the same way – that is, not as actual material ribs, but as a set of 'water-lines' in vertical planes which defined the ship's shape. In other words, if the ship were completely solid instead of being built up upon ribs, its shape could still be defined in the same way by assuming a number of arbitrary vertical planes through it.

Once the idea of imaginary planes had taken the place of actual ribs and water-lines, the way was open for describing on paper any solid streamlined body. The technique is shown in Fig. 36. This is a fairly modern drawing of a pilot boat, about 1900, but the technique was used much earlier with the later wooden ships and on the iron ships which followed. The shape is completely represented – by a series of curves in the front view, analogous to the ribs and represented by straight lines in the other two views; by a series of curves in the side view which appear as straight lines in the other views; and by a series of curves in the plan analogous to the water-lines, again appearing as straight lines in the front and side views. Given any one set of lines it is possible to derive the others. The system only holds good, of course, if the shape is such that any section gives a fair curve with no abrupt changes of form.

Shipbuilding, and particularly ship-draughting, advanced to quite a fine art. However, all trades in the Middle Ages and for some time later were kept rather secret by their practitioners, and the percolation of a technique from one trade to another was slow and often almost non-existent. All the same, a very similar technique for defining irregular shapes grew up in parallel through a different line of thought.

In 1738 the geographer Bauche turned some of his attention to marine charts. Whilst the sea-bed had form it was nevertheless a sort of shapeless form; its depth could be plumbed and the figures marked on a chart, provided the positions of the soundings were known. These figures gave, in effect, a picture of the sea-bed, for they gave an indication of the third dimension, that perpendicular to the sea surface or, on the chart, perpendicular to the paper. The more soundings taken and the more figures shown, the more complete was the picture. With sufficient figures it became possible to run continuous lines through like figures to produce what we would recognise as a contour map of the sea-bed. This, of course, is very

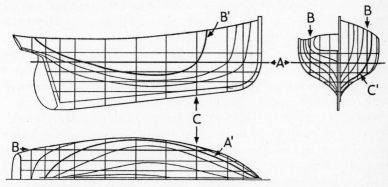

Fig. 36. A set of lines used to record the shape of a pilot boat about 1900. Each set of curves appears in the other two views as a series of straight lines.

close in nature to what we have just seen in ship draughting, because the various lines on the drawing of a ship were nothing more than a series of contour lines.

Linked with this was mapping or surveying on land and techniques developed steadily on the Continent of Europe largely through the demands made by the designers of fortifications. The geography and politics of Europe ensured an endless series of wars and, as soon as the so-called Age of Reason dawned, logic was applied to many fields of human activity including the waging of war. Through the Middle Ages the strong-point was the castle — more or less a keep with an outer wall round an enclosure. This gave way, with the advent of fire-arms, to fortifications, the science of which was expounded mainly by French generals, in particular Vauban and later Noizet.

British books on fortifications in the 18th century are mere shadows of the comparable French works. The English Channel made a natural barrier cutting Britain off from the Continent. Since invasion was most unlikely the study of fortifications was academic and half-hearted. The fort was conceived as being little more advanced than the older castles; and how scientific the approach was can be seen by following the method used for marking out a fort preparatory to building it. A table was placed at the centre of the proposed fort and the plan of the fort was stretched out on the table. Under the table was a stake to which a number of cords were attached. The engineer sighted along the lines on the plan running to the corners or towers of the fort and his assistant, holding the cord taut, was waved left or right until he had the cord laid out on the ground in line with the line on the plan. The distance along this line was scaled on the plan and measured out along the cord so that the tower's position could be marked by a stake. When all the stakes for all the towers were in position, cords stretched round them gave the line of the walls. This was probably much the same as the procedure used in building the earlier castles.[53]

On the Continent things were different. With their land boundaries any country could be invaded at any time and so the design of fortifications was taken seriously – too seriously perhaps in many cases, for the amount of technical effort put into the theoretical design of fortifications by the French seems rather out of proportion to the part that fortifications played in real wars. However, most of the theoretical and practical techniques developed in this field were able to be usefully applied in other fields, and this is but a further example of war or the threat of war hastening technical progress.

These continental fortifications were, in the plan view, elegant geometrical patterns. The inner fortifications were generally pentagonal or hexagonal and these were surrounded by extensive earthworks and ancilliary lines of defence giving, in plan, various star-shaped patterns. There was, of course, rationalism behind these patterns, for they were devised so that troops on the ramparts could give covering and cross-fire in all manner of contingencies. Fig. 37, taken from Diderot's famous encyclopedia of 1751, shows the plan of a typical fortification built partly of masonry and partly of earthworks.

A theoretical plan like this was, however, a long way from the actual building of such a fort. These fortifications covered very extensive areas compared with the old castles, and would measure some hundreds of yards across. The most advantageous site would naturally be chosen and the ground upon which it was to be con-

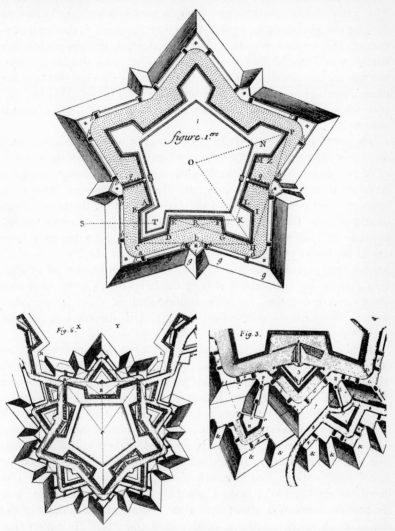

Fig. 37. Plans of fortifications from the middle 18th century. From Diderot's *Encyclopedia*, Vol. I, Art militaire, Fortification, Plate IV.

structed would usually be anything but flat. On the other hand, if the stringent requirements of the theoreticians were to be met, the actual slopes of the various earthworks and the heights of the walls and ramparts were important and could not be just guessed. This general problem was aggravated by two other requirements. The first was that the amount of earth to be moved should be a minimum. The other was somewhat more complicated and became known as defiling the fortification. In simple terms this meant first of all ascertaining the highest points in the surrounding terrain which the enemy could use to fire into the fort. The plane taken through the two highest such points and a third point within the fort was the plane of defilement and this was used as a basis for ascertaining the vertical heights of the fortification's parts instead of the horizontal plane.

To accommodate all these requirements it became more and more necessary to get a clear picture of the area; in other words effective maps were necessary and accordingly many advances were made in surveying techniques. The land, however, was of the same sort of shape as the sea-bed – if it were not for the water there would be little to distinguish them as far as essential form was concerned – and the natural solution was to use the same methods. One could not lower plumb-lines from some elevated plane as one could at sea, that is, from the sea surface. The determination of heights was a surveying problem, but once the heights at various positions were determined they could be represented on paper in the same way as depths were marked on a chart, with figures and contour lines.*

In place of the sea surface used for reference in marine charts, an arbitrary plane of comparison was selected. This might be below all the heights dealt with so that the point with the largest figure was the highest, but more often this plane was considered to be above the ground like an imaginary sea surface, in which case the highest point bore the lowest figure. This system in France became known as *plans côtés*. It later became of theoretical interest in Britain where the title was translated as 'figured plans'. By this time the need for large fortifications had virtually disappeared. It is of interest to note that the Civil War in the United States created an interest there in fortifications and about that time (1860) a Dr Mahan of the Military Academy wrote a book called *One Plane Descriptive Geometry* dealing with figured plans applied to fort design.

The figured plans system was not only used to map the terrain; it was also used to represent the various parts of the fortification and

---

* Contour lines for maps did not become general practice until the middle of the 19th century.

earthworks, and also the various theoretical planes, such as the plane of defilement. In other words, the system we would today associate through contour lines with irregular shapes, was applied to the definition of pure geometrical forms. Figured plans are of some importance in this story, for it was the revolt against this system which led Gaspard Monge to introduce his famous descriptive geometry doctrines. The works available before his time introduce figured plans amongst details of fortifications and are difficult to follow. The following quotation is from a later work of 1831* when the system was more complete, but it has the advantage that it deals only with geometrical principles. Although the quotation is rather long, it is given thus because there may be few draughtsmen who are in a position to obtain the French originals, although the whole system played an important part in drawing history (see Fig. 38).

Let us observe . . . that this method of description was used in the first instance for the depths of the sea-bed measured to sea-level, the prevailing practice being to calculate the vertical distances of 'height below' which may be regarded as veritable plumb-lines let down from a *plane of comparison* situated horizontally above all the objects considered; in this case the plane of projection is supposed horizontal and placed at an arbitrary distance *above* the objects. In general this particular convention will not render it more difficult to evaluate the difference in level of two points, but one must remember that it affects which figure is the *higher* or *lower* than the other.

From hereon a point in space will be represented by its projection (on a horizontal plane) and by its figure (or height in metres) as that indicated in *Fig. 1*. In consequence, if there are several separate points situated on the same vertical, it will be necessary to write the figures for each of them by the common projection.

A line is defined by its projection, AB, with the figures of two of its points. From that it will be easy by considering a trapezium standing on *AB*, to deduce graphically the length of a portion of this line, its inclination to the horizontal, the figure of a third point in this line, given by its projection, or vice versa the projection of a point defined by this figure. But since, for the application we have in view here, it will be better to finish with these results in terms of numbers to the true scale of the drawing, it will be more exact and in general more useful to construct first the *scale of inclination* of the proposed line. Assuming, therefore, that *A* and *B* are the projections of the two points whose figures are 14·7 m. and 12·5 m., one

* This is translated from a section of Leroy's book (Ref. 44) of 1867, but the author states that it is a condensed version of lectures given at Mézières by Capt. Génie Noizet in 1831.

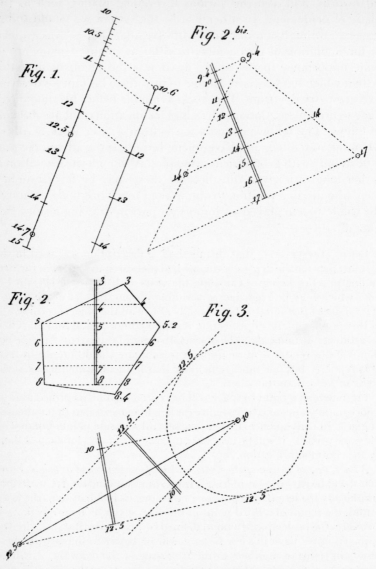

Fig. 38. Some elements of the figured plans method of drawing, taken from Leroy's *Traité de géométrie descriptive*, 1867, Plate 64, Vol. 2.

begins by seeking the interval, L, which, on the projection of the line, will separate two points whose figures *differ by one metre*, and one will arrive at the following proportion:–

$$\frac{14\cdot 7 \text{ m.} - 12\cdot 5 \text{ m.}}{AB} : \frac{1 \text{ m.}}{L} \quad L = \frac{5\,AB}{11}$$

and, having measured AB in terms of the horizontal scale of the drawing and found it to be 6·8 m., one can further deduce

$$L = 3\cdot 1 \text{ m. and } 0\cdot 3L = 0\cdot 9 \text{ m.}$$

Then, taking on the horizontal scale an opening of the compass equal to 0·9 m. and carrying it onto line AB above the point 14·7 m. one will obtain that point which will have the figure 15 m.; after that, if one sets off from this last point the length L several times in series, one will find the points which correspond to the figures 14 m., 13 m., 12 m., etc.; and finally it will only remain to sub-divide one of these intervals into ten equal parts to complete the *scale of inclination* of the proposed line. This constant length, L, can be called the unit of the scale of inclination. . . .

To find the true distance between two points on this line given their projections. One will first find these points' figures; then one will calculate the hypotenuse of a right-angled triangle of which the height will be *the difference of these figures*, and of which the base will be, *to scale, the interval of the two projections*, estimated in metres on the horizontal scale of the drawing. Thus for the two points projected as A and B, the true distance will be given by the formula:

$$d = \sqrt{(2\cdot 2)^2 + (6\cdot 8)^2} = 7\cdot 1 \text{ m.}$$

A plane (*Fig. 2*), which really exists and is, in consequence, limited in all its parts, is represented by the projection of its perimeter, every angle having its figure; and one may add a certain number of *sections of level*, which are lines parallel to its horizontal trace. These sections, which are chosen equidistant and spaced apart by, for example, one metre *in the vertical sense*, will each be marked at their two extremities by a common figure; then if one draws at right-angles to these horizontals a line, it will become that which we have called the scale of inclination of the plane, and which is generally indicated by a double tracked line.

When a plane is unlimited and does not exist in reality, one represents it only by one of its figured horizontals with its scale of inclination graduated (*Fig. 2 bis*). Often it is sufficient to make just the graduated scale, as from that one can produce as many horizontals as one wishes, since they are always at right angles to the scale. . . .

Through a given line construct a plane whose inclination is $1/n$. (*Fig. 3*). One must know at least the figures for two points of this line, which are here 10 m. and 12·5 m.; therefore regarding the superior point, 10 m., as the summit of a right cone of which the generator will have the inclination $1/n$, it will be sufficient to construct a plane tangent to this cone and passing through the second point. But if one describes a circle which has for its centre the projection of the point 10 m., and for its radius a length, taken from the horizontal scale of the drawing, equal to n times the difference 2·5 m. of the figures of the given points, then this circle will be the trace of the cone in question on the horizontal plane which passes through the inferior point, 12·5 m. Therefore, in drawing through the last point two tangents to this circle, one obtains the horizontal traces of two planes which satisfy the conditions; and their scales of inclination may be easily deduced for one has their directions and two figured points in each.[44]

The above quotation, long as it is, barely introduces the system as it was eventually developed. Figured plans have an inherent interest of their own, and parts of the system are used today in map-making and surveying, but apart from this there are other reasons for the introduction of this subject into the story. As mentioned earlier, it was the rebellion of the young Monge against such long-winded, and to him obscure, operations which prompted him to develop the system of drawing christened descriptive geometry. Whilst Monge rejected the figured plans system as a whole, he nevertheless generalised certain parts and incorporated them in his doctrine, with the result that, in a sense, draughtsmen use figured plans in their everyday work but in a disguised form.

8

Descartes: Linking Geometry and Algebra

In this chapter we are going to see very briefly the correlation which arose between geometry and mathematics. This is not essential to our story, but it is included because it is relevant to a full understanding of the development of modern technical drawing. Some of Gaspard Monge's thinking was based on mathematical ideas of shape and if, in dealing later with his descriptive geometry, we ignore this we shall have a slightly distorted picture. Later also we shall see how there is a trend towards using computers for drawing purposes, and computers are essentially mathematical machines, so that a knowledge of shape in terms of algebra is necessary to understand this recent development.

We are particularly concerned here with co-ordinate geometry, the invention of René Descartes (1596–1650) which successfully connected geometry and algebra.

Descartes had a mathematical training although he is known to most persons as a philosopher. Even while he was at school he began to wonder how mankind professed to know so many 'truths'. So many ideas were put across to him dogmatically and his analyses of these ideas caused him to doubt many, if not all, things.

At this time the ancient Greek learning had been rediscovered and, after some struggle, had been adopted by the Church. Questioning of the ancient beliefs was tantamount to an attack on the Church, hence the dogmatic nature of teaching. However, Descartes lived late in the Renaissance period when many thinkers were challenging the ideas hitherto accepted for hundreds or thousands of years. It was the time of Isaac Newton (1642–1727), Gottfried Wilhelm Leibniz (1646–1716), Galileo Galilei (1564–1642), Blaise Pascal (1623–1662), Gérard Desargues (1593–1662) and Pierre de Fermat (1601–1665), amongst many others who laid the foundations of our modern scientific world with their questioning of ancient beliefs and promulgation of new thinking.

Over the years, Descartes gave great thought to how one could obtain truths and at length he decided that only the methods of geometers and mathematicians, which used a succession of simple reasonings leading from primary axioms to the most difficult demonstrations, seemed useful. He therefore determined to examine and record these thinking methods as a new basis for philosophical reasoning.

The principles he settled upon were, firstly, that he would accept nothing as true which was not so clear and distinct in his mind that there was no room for doubt; secondly, he would divide up large problems into smaller ones; thirdly, that he would proceed from the simple to the complex; and fourthly, that he would enumerate and examine all the steps of his reasoning so thoroughly that there would be little chance of some oversight.

He expounded his ideas in a famous work of 1637 called *Discourse on Method*. His 'Geometrical Matters' was attached to this as a sort of extensive appendix and was used to exhibit the practical application of his method of reasoning to geometry—rather analogous to what Archimedes and many other ancient Greeks had done. His geometrical work was very opportune. Geometry up to this time was essentially the ancient Euclidean, which confined itself to figures formed by straight lines and circles. Ellipses, parabolas and hyperbolas (the conic sections) were known, of course, from the times of ancient Greece, but understanding of these shapes was limited. Desargues wrote some original work on these conic sections and, as they were in touch with one another, Descartes was aware of most of Desargues's contributions to geometry. Published almost in the same year as Descartes's work was Galileo's *Two New Sciences* in which, amongst much else, he showed that the path of a cannonball was a parabola; Johann Kepler (1571–1630) had shown that the orbits of the planets were ellipses; the best curves for the lenses of the newly invented telescopes and microscopes proved to be other than parts of spheres; and later Leonhard Euler (1707–1783) and others studying the optimum shapes for gear teeth turned to cycloids and involutes. All round, there was a pressing need to deal with these new curves by new methods, since the Euclidean concepts were, at best, clumsy and, at worst, inadequate.

Everything, naturally, grows out of that which precedes it. The idea of defining the position of a point in a plane by its co-ordinates was, in itself, extremely old. Map-making in the ancient civilisations only covered small areas and places were quoted by reference to their 'widths' and 'lengths', from which came our terms 'latitude' and 'longitude'. We still use this today in engineering drawings whenever we dimension from two datum edges, and this method was used by Descartes to develop a system of defining curves by algebraical equations which governed the positions of all the individual points making up a line.

For our present purpose it is not so much Descartes's work itself which is of interest, as much as the later development of this from two to three dimensions. Descartes's *Geometrical Matters* covered roughly 120 pages and dealt with much which is only of interest to mathematicians, so we willc onfine our observations to a few general points.

To illustrate the power of his new reasoning methods, Descartes took the problem of Pappus; the details of this need not concern us, but it had, until that time, been incapable of solution except for certain special cases. He decided to show how this problem could be solved in general for all cases.

To solve the problem of Pappus, Descartes had to deal with curves unknown, that is undefinable, at that time. His general thesis was as follows. A point results from the intersection of two lines. If the two lines are moving, then their point of intersection will move, tracing out a curve, and by building up suitable sets of linkages, or sets of 'rulers', one could thus generate any required curve. To demonstrate this idea, Descartes put forward Fig. 39, about which he said:

This instrument consists of several rulers hinged together in such a way that YZ being placed along the line AN the angle XYZ can be increased or decreased in size, and when its sides are together the points B, C, D, E, F, G, H, all coincide with A; but as the size of the angle increases, the ruler BC, fastened at right angles to XY at the point B, pushes towards Z the ruler CD which slides along YZ always at right angles. In like manner, CD pushes DE which slides along YX always parallel to BC; DE pushes EF; EF pushes FG; FG pushes GH, and so on. Thus we may imagine an infinity of rulers, each pushing another, half of them making equal angles with YX and the rest with YZ.

Now as the angle XYZ is increased the point B describes the curve AB, which is a circle; while the intersections of the other rulers, namely the points D, F, H, describe other curves, AD, AF, AH, of which the latter are more complex than the first and this more complex than the circle. Nevertheless, I see no reason why the description of the first cannot be conceived as clearly and distinctly as that of the second, third, or any other that can be thus, described, cannot be as clearly conceived of as the first; and, therefore, I see no reason why they should not be used in the same way in the solution of geometric problems. [24]

Any chosen point of intersection in Fig. 39, say D, could addition ally be defined by quoting its perpendicular distance from a fixed line – say the distance DC from line YZ – and the distance of this perpendicular from some fixed point in the line – say CY measured from Y. Because the point D is generated by the rulers it is possible to relate the distances DC and CY in a generalised way which will hold good for all positions of point D, and thus this relationship will accurately define the curve.

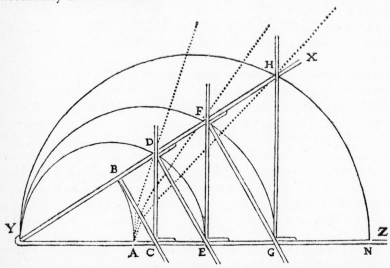

Fig. 39. A theoretical arrangement of rulers devised by Descartes to generate mechanically a number of curves not at that time known, but which would be amenable to description in terms of algebra as easily as other curves, such as the conic sections. From *Discours de la méthode*, by René Descartes, 'Des Matières de la géométrie', pp. 318 and 370, 1637.

In Fig. 39 let us call the radius BY, a, and the variable distance along the ruler DY, z, whilst referring to the vertical distance DC as y, and the horizontal distance CY as x. Then by similar triangles $z : x = x : a$, hence $z = x^2/a$. By Pythagoras $z^2 = x^2 + y^2$. Combining the two equations gives $x^4 = a^2(x^2 + y^2)$ as the equation of the curve. In this way Descartes combined geometry, that is, shape, with algebra. The change of outlook was considerable. For instance, to Pythagoras (if symbols of this kind had then been in use) $z^2 = x^2 + y^2$ would have meant that the area of a square drawn on the hypotenuse of a right-angled triangle was equivalent to the combined areas of the squares drawn on the other two sides. In the geometry of Descartes the same expression represents an infinite number of points which in total describe a circle of radius z. Similarly other equations can describe particular parabolas, hyperbolas and many other curves which in those times had no names.

Descartes restricted his geometrical excursion to the field of plane geometry, but he was well aware of its three-dimensional possibilities and we read at the end of the Second Book of *Geometrical Matters*:

> In all this discussion I have considered only curves that can be described upon a plane surface, but my remarks can easily be made to apply to all those curves which can be conceived of as generated by the regular movement of the points of a body in three-dimensional space. This can be done by dropping perpendiculars from each point of the curve under consideration upon two planes intersecting at right angles, for the ends of these perpendiculars will describe two other curves, one in each of the two planes, all points of which may be determined in the way already explained, and all of which may be related to those of a straight line common to the two planes; and by means of these the points of the three-dimensional curve will be entirely determined. [24]

Descartes did not illustrate this idea, considering his explanation in words sufficient to make his point. As we shall see, Gaspard Monge's descriptive geometry owed much to this idea.

The combining of shape, in the form of geometry, with algebra was a step of great significance and naturally it was built upon by many others. Leibniz turned his attention to the slopes of curves at particular points and so developed the differential calculus at about the time Newton was making the same discoveries. Many others, including Parent (1666–1736), Clairaut (1713–1765), Van Schooten (d. 1661) and Monge (1746–1818), followed up Descartes's work, one of the most obvious routes being to transfer his geometry of two dimensions into three dimensions.

When one does this everything moves up, as it were, to a higher dimension. $A = mx + ny$ represents a straight line in a two-dimensional plane. $A = mx + ny + pz$, however, does not represent a straight line in three-dimensional space; instead it represents a plane. In a similar way, as $R^2 = mx^2 + ny^2$ is the formula for a circle, so $R^2 = mx^2 + ny^2 + pz^2$ is that of a spherical surface. Although it does not concern us here, it is interesting to note that by analogy it is possible to extrapolate these ideas into four dimensions; one can deal with equations with four variables – which give hyperplanes, hyperspheres and so on – although these forms do not correspond with our visual interpretation of the world.

One can manipulate algebraic equations in many ways and, since these equations can represent geometrical forms, it becomes of interest to ascertain what such manipulations mean in terms of geometry. For instance, let us take two equations—each of which represents a plane—and see what happens if we treat them simultaneously.

$$3x + 3y + 4z = 12$$
$$4x + 3y + 2z = 10$$

If we take the second from the first, we get

$$2z - x = 2$$

and we might well wonder what this last equation represents.

Since the two equations are treated simultaneously, the result

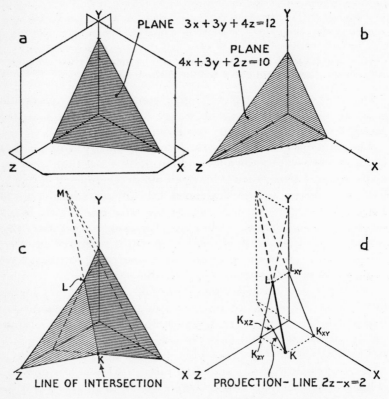

Fig. 40. (a) Three reference planes XY, YZ and XZ, mutually at right angles with a plane defined pictorially by its intersections with the reference planes.

(b) A second plane defined by its traces on the reference planes.

(c) The two planes intersecting in a line in space.

(d) The line in space projected on to the reference planes.

must appertain to the line in which the planes intersect, since this is the only part of both which is common. Yet if we plot this equation it becomes a line in the XZ plane, as it must because there is no y term. When we treated the two above equations simultaneously we eliminated the y term and this, in a space representation, is tantamount to eliminating a dimension. If we do this and compress everything into two dimensions then we have a *projection* of the line in space–and this is, indeed, what the equation $2z - x = 2$ represents.

These space relationships are mapped out in Fig. 40 where we have three reference planes mutually at right angles, XY, YZ and XZ, the axes where they intersect being the three lines X, Y and Z. In (c) we see the two planes defined by the two given equations and in (d) the line represented by the equation $2z - x = 2$ is shown as the projection of the line of intersection of the planes. If the two original equations are treated simultaneously to eliminate successively x and then z, the equations resulting will be the projections of the line in space upon the YZ and XY planes respectively.

There is no need for us to follow this mathematical excursion any further, but it is useful to bear in mind the relationship between algebra and geometry, and in particular how the *elimination* of one unknown in a pair of equations gives the *projection* of that which is common to the two forms represented by the equations. The reason, as we shall see in the next chapter, is that at a particular point in his life Monge worked extensively in the mathematics of three-dimensional co-ordinate geometry and this was to give his drawing doctrines a basic philosophy distinctly different from those with empirical origins.

9

Monge : The Birth of Descriptive Geometry

ONE of the most intriguing books in the history of technical drawing is Gaspard Monge's *Géométrie descriptive* published in 1795. Although Monge is known on the Continent as the Father of Descriptive Geometry, neither he nor his work are well known in the English-speaking world, for reasons which we shall see later. Some short writings on the history of drawing have noted that Monge invented the set of techniques known as descriptive geometry and that, as engineering drawing is based on descriptive geometry, he played a significant part in the development of modern industrial drawing. To some extent this is true, but it is not true in the simple sense that the above reasoning implies, especially so far as Britain, the Commonwealth and America are concerned.

Unlike Descartes's work, the significance of which is beyond dispute for all time, Monge's descriptive geometry appeared to be very important at the time it was introduced, though over the intervening years its real worth has beome more and more difficult to assess. This assessment is, today, probably very much a matter of opinion and depends largely upon the kind of drawing education one has had. Rather than try to make an assessment for the reader, this fascinating story will be unfolded in this and subsequent chapters so that one can judge for oneself.

Gaspard Monge was born at Beaune, near Dijon in France, in 1746. His father was a business man of humble fortune, though he made great efforts to see that his three sons were educated to the best of his ability. Gaspard showed unusual promise in mathematics and science, and at length he was recommended to the Commandant of the school founded some years previously at Mézières for officers of the Army. As one might have expected, the humble nature of Monge's parents made him unsuitable for acceptance as a student officer. The Commandant, however, offered him a place as a student draughtsman in the fortification design office, and Monge accepted. Although Monge turned out in the long run to be a remarkable scholar, this unusual beginning led directly to the birth of his descriptive geometry.

Monge, through his mathematical training, had a tidy, logical mind, and the various drawing methods with which he was confronted in this design office offended him. At best they were, to him, inelegant, and the worst of them he considered to be barbarous empirical approximations. Dexterity of hand, he said later, prevailed over intelligence. His innate abilities were completely ignored until, having a mathematical background, he was selected by the Commandant to make all the practical calculations for a defilement operation on a fortification. The methods Monge was supposed to use were similar to those we have previously seen in the method of figured plans, in which only the plan was used and all the heights and angles of slope were calculated from the basic figures on the plan. 'Repulsed by the long and tedious gropings through which one arrived at the solution, and wanting to shine at the beginning of his career', Monge evolved a new, entirely geometrical, method which he used on the problem. The solution was, of course, contested because he had spent far less time on the job than was normally expected. However, since the Commandant might have had to take disciplinary action, he had no option but to examine the student's work.

He recognised at once Monge's true worth and, as one might expect, took him out of the drawing-office. Monge became a pupil of, and later assistant to, the professor of physics and had started off on the two main branches of his life – science and teaching.

We shall never know exactly what Monge did to effect this 'promotion' but, in principle, it was probably very close to the initial techniques expounded much later in his book. The following selected quotations will serve to demonstrate these ideas:

> The surfaces of all material bodies can be considered as made up of points, and the first step we are going to make in this treatise must be to indicate how one can express the position of a point in space.
>
> Space is without limit; all parts of space are alike; there is nothing characteristic about any particular part so it can serve as a term of reference for indicating the position of a particular point.
>
> Thus, to define the position of a point in space it is necessary to refer this position to those of other objects which are of known position in some distinctive part of space, the number of objects being as many as are required to define the point; and for the process to be amenable for easy and daily use, it is necessary that these objects should be the simplest possible so that their positions can be easily imagined.

Monge then, and at some length, examined the possibilities of using points, then lines and finally planes as the 'objects of known position'. In other words, he showed that a point in space could be defined by giving its distances from three planes or, if these were mutually at right angles as we saw in the chapter on co-ordinate geometry, by giving the point's three co-ordinates. He then continued:

. . . in descriptive geometry, which has been practised for a long time by a large number of persons and by many to whom time was precious,* the process can again be simplified, and instead of considering three planes we find that by means of projections we only have need of two.

The projection of a point on a plane may be defined as the foot of the perpendicular lowered from the point onto the plane.

It follows, that if on two planes of known position in space one is given on each the projection of the point whose position one wishes to define, this point will be perfectly determined.

In effect, if from the projection on the first plane one constructs a perpendicular to this plane, it is evident that it will pass through the point defined. Likewise, if from its projection on the second plane one constructs a perpendicular to the plane, it passes likewise through the defined point. Therefore the point will be uniquely at their intersection and is accordingly perfectly determined.

In the following paragraphs we will show how to make easy use of this and the method used to make drawings on flat sheets of paper.

Fig. 3.† If, from all the points on a straight line of indefinite length AB oriented in any direction in space, one can imagine perpendiculars dropped to a plane $LMNO$, in some given position, all the points at the meeting of these perpendiculars with the plane will lie on another straight line of indefinite length, ab; for they will all lie in the plane passing through AB lying perpendicular to plane $LMNO$, and they will only be able to meet the latter at the common intersection of two planes, which is a straight line.

The line ab on the plane $LMNO$, which is formed by the projection of all the points from another line AB, is called the projection of the line AB on the plane.

Since two points are sufficient to fix the position of a straight line, to construct the projection of a straight line it is only necessary to project these two points, the projection of the line passing through the two points where the projectors meet the plane.

Fig. 2.† Being given, on two non-parallel planes, $LMNO$ and $LMPQ$, the projections ab and $a'b'$ of the line AB, the position of the line AB is fully determined; for if through one of the projections ab one imagines a plane perpendicular to $LMNO$, this plane, of known position, must necessarily pass through the line AB; likewise, if through the projection $a'b'$

* This may refer to the delay in publishing his work, but it is more likely an admission that similar practices had been used empirically for some centuries.
† Of Fig. 41 in this book.

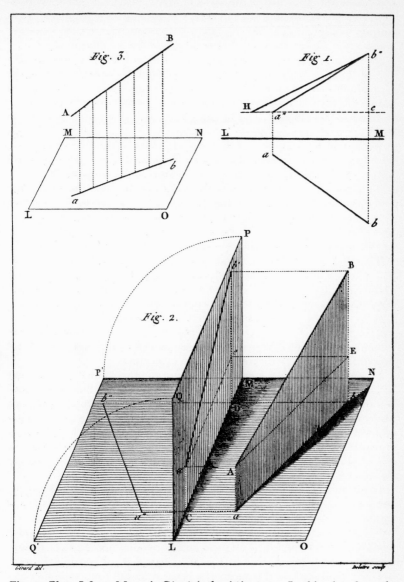

Fig. 41. Plate I from Monge's *Géométrie descriptive*, 1795. In this plate from the first edition 'Fig. 1' was erroneously engraved as 'Fig. 3' and vice versa.

one imagines a plane perpendicular to $LMPQ$, this plane, of known position, also passes through the line AB. The position of this line, which is simultaneously on two known planes, is consequently at their common intersection and its position, therefore, is absolutely determined. . . .

As the majority of draughtsmen who will practise this method are already familiar with the position of a horizontal plane and the direction of a plumb-line, they will be quite used to supposing that of the two planes of projection, one is horizontal and the other vertical.

The need for making the drawings of the two projections on a single sheet and for carrying out the operations in the same area, calls for the draughtsman to imagine that the vertical plane is turned about its intersection with the horizontal plane, like a hinge, to lie flat in the horizontal plane, and it is in this state that he will construct his projections.

Thus the vertical projection is always drawn on the horizontal plane and it is necessary to imagine that it is raised up and put back into place by means of a quarter revolution about the intersection of the horizontal and vertical planes. It is necessary, accordingly, that this intersection line be made so that it can be clearly seen on the drawing.

Therefore, in Fig. 2* the projection $a'b'$ of the line AB is not executed on a plane which is really vertical; one imagines that the plane is turned about the axis LM to the position $LMP'Q'$ and it is in this position of the plane that one carries out the vertical projection of $a''b''$. . . .

As yet the straight line AB has been considered of indefinite length and its direction only has been considered; but if we regard it as being limited by the points A and B, it may be necessary to know its length, which we proceed to determine by way of its two projections.

When a straight line is parallel to one of the two planes of projection its length is equal to its projection on this plane; for the line and its projection, being both terminated by two perpendiculars to the plane of projection, are parallel to each other and joined at their extremities by parallel lines. In this case then, when the projection is given, the length of the straight line, which is equal to it, is also given. It is evident that a straight line is parallel to one of the two planes when its projection on the other is parallel to their intersections (line LM).

If a straight line is oblique to each of the two planes, then its length is greater than either of its projections, but may be deduced from them very simply.

Let AB be a straight line whose projections ab and $a'b'$ are given and whose length is required. If we suppose a horizontal line AE to be drawn through one of its extremities A in the vertical plane passing through AB, and produced until it meets the vertical let fall from the other extremity in the point E, a right-angled triangle, AEB, will be formed which is to be constructed in order to obtain the length of the line AB, which is the hypotenuse. Now, besides knowing the angle E to be a right

* Of Fig. 41 in this book.

angle, we also know that AE is equal in length to the given projection ab. Also drawing in the vertical plane through a', a horizontal line $a'e$, it cuts the vertical $b'D$ at the point e, which is the projection of the point E; and therefore $b'e$ is the vertical projection of BE, and the same in length. Hence, having determined the lengths of the two sides containing the right-angle, there will be no difficulty in constructing the hypotenuse of the triangle, AB.

Fig. 2,* being in perspective, has no resemblance to the construction used in the method of projections; we are here going to give the construction of this first question in all its simplicity.

Fig. 1.* The line LM, being supposed to be the intersection of the two planes of projection, and the lines ab and $a''b''$ being the given projections of a straight line, to find the length of this line one takes through the point a'' the horizontal He, which will cut the line bb'' in a point e, and upon this horizontal one will transfer ab from e to H. One will then take the hypotenuse Hb'', and the length of this hypotenuse will be that of the required line.

From the above, one sees that if one has the two projections of a body terminated by plane faces, by rectilineal edges and by solid angles, the projections of which become a system of lines, it will be easy to find the length of any dimension one may wish, for such a dimension will be parallel to one of the two planes of projection or it will be oblique to both. In the first case the length required will be equal to its projection; in the second, one will deduce it from its two projections through the procedure given above.[51]

This quotation summarises the first set of principles which collectively Monge designated 'Descriptive Geometry'. His solution to the defilement operation was probably made up of a series of repetitions of the operation described above, for the latter is directly connected with the method of figured plans. In the chapter dealing with this method a sloping line in space was defined by its plan, that is its projection onto the vertical plane, with two figures at its extremities. To find the length or slope of the line one imagined a trapezium standing on the line's plan and worked out the information required by trigonometry. All Monge did here was actually to draw this trapezium upon a vertical plane. When a line in plan was not parallel to the vertical plane of projection, he simply 're-volved' the line till it was parallel. That is, referring to his Fig. 1, he figuratively swung ab about b as centre until it was parallel to LM, when the projection of A would be at H on the vertical plane. The similarity between Monge's technique here and the method of figured plans is striking and it is worth turning back to make a comparison.

* Of Fig. 41 in this book.

Although Monge had moved on to physics he did not forget his drawing excursion. At Mézières there were schools of stone-cutting and carpentry, since most of the military works of the time were still of stone and wood in the main. He set about examining the drawing methods used by stone-cutters and carpenters, and applied his first principles of descriptive geometry to them in order to replace many rote techniques with generalised methods. He had a lot of success in the field of stone-cutting and his ideas were adopted at the school. He came across stubborn opposition from the carpenters, however, who were relying on drawing techniques passed on from father to son for generations and who saw no reason for an academic person to butt in. Indeed, twenty years were to pass before he has a similar success with carpentry at the school.

All the same, he had accumulated enough material to write a book on his methods applied to fortifications, stone-cutting and carpentry, and he was greatly disappointed when the authorities forbade him to publish his ideas. The military engineers 'from a small-minded sense of wishing to remain superior to other schools' decided that descriptive geometry should remain 'within the confines of the School at Mézières' and they did this very effectively by classing it as a military secret.

It is difficult to tell what sort of a book Monge would have written at this time if he were able, but we can make a fair surmise by applying the axioms of Monge described above to the stone-cutting problem previously solved by Desargues in an earlier chapter.

Fig. 42 shows the plan and side view of the block of stone – that is the projections of the stone onto Monge's two planes of projection – which exhibit the primary angles. The compound angles would be determined by 'revolving' the faces in question until they were parallel to the planes of projection. For example, to find the true shape of the 'battered' face $VWXY$, this face in elevation would be revolved from AB to $A''B$ and A'' projected down to give the shape $V'WXY''$ in the plan. Similarly XYZ in the plan would be revolved to $X'Y'Z$ parallel to LM and the points projected upwards to give $A'B'CD$. We have here revolved complete faces; Monge might have only revolved the relevant triangular portions. In any case, the real point to note is that in such a construction the drawing exhibits both a representation of the block – instead of just the angles as in Desargues's construction – and also a really generalised method for determining the shapes of inclined faces. In other words, the 'picture' idea and the methods of geometrically deducing information about three-dimensional forms – graphical geometry – had been combined. The elegance of this general solution caused great admiration at the time – although it looks simple enough to us – and many were apt to see more in it than there really was. Clever as this Mongean solution was, it does not, in fact, give us any more information than the earlier methods, though it demonstrates this information in a clearer way.

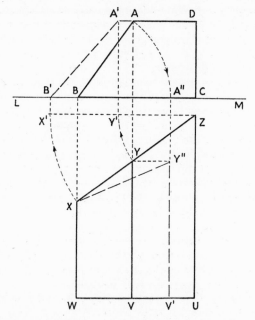

Fig. 42. Monge's descriptive geometry axioms used to determine the compound angles for the block illustrated in Fig. 33 where the problem was solved by Desargues's method.

Although Monge was forbidden to publish his ideas, this edict did not stifle his thinking or his hope and we now come to the second step in this story. If one reads carefully the quotation above one will notice that it has much in common with what we previously came across in co-ordinate geometry; a line in space, for instance, being obtained by the intersection of two planes and being represented by its projections. Monge, being mathematically trained, also noticed the similarity and, unable to develop his descriptive geometry along practical lines, he turned to considering his ideas more abstractly, correlating them with algebra.

This new excursion is summarised, in a way, by another quotation from his book, although it was written many years later.

In algebra, when a problem is expressed in terms of equations and one has as many equations as unknowns, one can always obtain the same number of equations in which enters only one unknown; through this we can obtain the values of each of them. The operation by which one does this, and which is called *elimination*, consists of expelling one of the unknowns from all the equations by manipulating them, and by successively expelling the different unknowns one arrives at a final equation which contains only one unknown, whose value may then be found.

The object of elimination in algebra has the greatest analogy with the operations through which, in descriptive geometry, one determines the intersections of curved surfaces.

Indeed, let us suppose that, considering a point in space and representing by x, y, z the distances of this point from three mutually perpendicular planes, one establishes a relation between the three distances, and that this relation is expressed by an equation in which enter the three quantities x, y, z and constants. By virtue of this relation the point will not be determined, for the quantities x, y, z can change in value and consequently the point can change position in space without the relation expressed by the equation ceasing to hold; and the curved surface, which passes through all the positions the point can occupy without the relationship between these three co-ordinates being altered, is that to which the equation pertains.

For example, let us suppose a sphere of radius A has its centre at the point of common intersection of the three mutually perpendicular planes; and that in considering a certain point on the surface of the sphere, one imagines perpendiculars dropped from this point onto the three planes and represented by the letters x, y, z; it is evident that the radius of the sphere, directed to the point considered, will be the diagonal of a rectangular prism, of which the three edges will be x, y, z; that its square will be equal to the sum of the squares of the three edges; and that, therefore, one will have the equation $x^2 + y^2 + z^2 = A^2$.

If the point changes its position on the sphere its distances x, y, z to the three perpendicular planes will change; but its distance from the centre will not, and the sum of the squares of the three co-ordinates, which is always equal to the square of the radius, will always have the same value; and one will thus have again between the co-ordinates of this point, the relation expressed by the equation $x^2 + y^2 + z^2 = A^2$. This equation, which holds for all the points of the sphere's surface and which holds for them only, is that of the surface. All curved surfaces have, thus, each their equation; and if it is not always easy to have this equation expressed in quantities as simple as the distances x, y, z, it is always possible to obtain it in more complicated quantities. . . .

Now, if having in x, y, z the equations of two different curved surfaces, and supposing that for the points of the two surfaces, the distances being taken with respect to the same perpendicular planes, one eliminates one of the three quantities x, y, z, for example z, between the two equations; by the simultaneousness of these two equations one establishes first that this is not of all the points on the first surface, nor of all those of the second, but only of those of their intersection, for each of which the two equations must hold, since they are at the same time on the two surfaces. Then the equation in x, y which results from the elimination of z, expresses the relation which exists between these two distances for the points of intersection, the distance z having disappeared and being no longer in the equation; it is thus the equation of the intersection of the two surfaces on the plane perpendicular to z.

One sees therefore that in algebra the object of elimination between several equations of three unknowns is to determine upon the three planes to which all space is referred, the projections of the intersections of surfaces to which the equations pertain.[51]

Taken on its own this quotation might be a lot to digest. However, with the chapter on co-ordinate geometry as a background, it is clear that this merely extends the ideas previously expounded into the realm of curves and curved lines instead of simple planes and straight lines.

Monge did a great deal of work in this mathematical field and published many of his results in the Memoirs of the Academy of Sciences,* together with other scientific papers, for the express purpose of gaining membership of that body which he did at the age of 34 in 1780.

Monge's excursion into three-dimensional co-ordinate geometry had repercussions on his descriptive geometry ideas. In dealing with co-ordinate geometry, we saw that planes in space could be represented by their traces upon the reference planes and Monge absorbed this into his drawing doctrine. His mathematical work also led him to an unusual insight into the conceiving of curved surfaces in space and of the intersections of such surfaces. Monge also noticed that all the curves dealt with mathematically were *generated*, that is they could be defined in clear unambiguous terms. He suddenly realised that all the solid geometrical forms in which we were interested were generated shapes – indeed it was the very methods of their generation which allowed us to conceive or recognise them. This concept was unconsciously known to everyone – just as it is known to us today – but Monge decided that great advantages would accrue if people were made consciously aware of the generated

* A book was also written later, *Application de l'analyse à la géométrie*, 1795.

nature of regular shapes since such knowledge could be put to use primarily in descriptive geometry, but also in other directions.

The following quotations are rather long, but they have been selected and recorded in full because they demonstrate the elegance with which Monge fitted these new ideas in with his earlier methods of projection, and with each other.

The convention employed as the basis of the method of projections is well adapted to express the position of a point in space, and for that of expressing a straight line of limited or unlimited length and, consequently, for representing the form and position of a body bounded by plane faces, by rectilineal edges and by solid angles; because in this instance a body is completely known when we know the positions of all its edges and of the vertices of all its angles. But should the body be bounded either by one curved surface having all its points subject to the same law, as in the case of a sphere,* or by the several parts of different curved surfaces, as in the case of a body whose surface has been formed on a lathe, this convention will not only be inconvenient and impracticable, but will be insufficient for accomplishing the object proposed and incapable of further development.

In the first place it is evident that this convention when taken singly would be inconvenient; for in order to express the position of the points of a curved surface, not only must each be distinguished by its horizontal and vertical projections, but these projections must be so connected that the horizontal projection of one point shall not be mistaken for that which corresponds to the vertical projection of another; and as the most simple method of connecting these two projections is to join them by a straight line perpendicular to the line of intersection of the planes of projection, by the application of this method a drawing would be crowded with a prodigious number of lines. And the more exact we might wish to draw the figure, the more confusion would exist. . . .

It is necessary, therefore, to have recourse to an additional convention which shall be consistent with the first and shall, at the same time, supply that in which it is deficient. . . .

Every curved surface may be regarded as generated by the movement of a line, either constant in form while it changes its position, or variable at the same time both in form and in position in space; a proposition which, since it may not be so easily understood in this general form, we shall explain by taking a few examples with which we are already familiar. . . .

Cylindrical surfaces may be generated in two principal ways, either by the movement of a straight line which always remains parallel to a given

---

* Notice that while a circle can be regarded as a 'picture' of a sphere, it is an inadequate projection of a sphere's surface, hence the earlier stereographic and orthographic projections of the sphere which used lines of longitude and latitude.

straight line, while it moves so as to pass through all the points of a given curve,* or by the movement of the curve which in the first method served as a guide for the straight line, in such a way that, one of its points moving along a given straight line, all the other points may describe lines parallel to this line. In both these methods the generating line, which in the first case was a straight line and in the second a curve, is constant in form and only changes its position . . .

It is evident that all curved surfaces may be generated by the movement of certain curved lines, and that there is not any surface whose form and position cannot be completely determined by an exact and complete definition of its mode of generation. This new consideration constitutes the complement to the method of projections, and we shall frequently have occasion, as we proceed, to observe its simplicity and use.

The form and position of a curved surface is not, then, determined by knowing the projections of the particular points through which it passes, but by being able to construct the generating curve through any point according to the form and position which belong to it in passing through this point; and here it should be observed that firstly each curved surface may be generated in an infinite number of ways, and that the ingenuity and skill of the constructor are shown in selecting that which employs the most simple curve and is the most easily understood; and secondly that experience has shown us that instead of regarding a curved surface as generated by one curve in one particular manner, which requires a knowledge of the law of the curve's motion and also its change of form, it is preferable to consider two different methods of generating the surface at the same time, and point out the construction for the two generating curves through each point.

Therefore, in descriptive geometry, in order to express the form and position of a curved surface, it is sufficient to give for any point whatsoever on this surface, whose projections may be taken at pleasure, the method for constructing the horizontal and vertical projections of the two different generating curves which pass through the point.

Let us now apply these general considerations to a plane, which of all surfaces is the most simple and the most frequently employed in geometrical constructions.

A plane may be regarded as generated by a straight line whose primary position is given, and which moves in such a manner that each of its points describes a straight line parallel to a second given straight line; if this second straight line is situated in the plane we are considering, we may also say that the plane is generated by the second straight line moving so that all its points describe straight lines parallel to the first.

A good idea of the position of a plane is thus afforded us by the consideration of two straight lines, either of which may be looked upon as

---

* The term 'cylinder' throughout Monge's work meant, in general, a prism the section of which was a figure enclosed in a curve, the curve not necessarily being a circle.

generating it; and the position of these lines in the plane which they generate is immaterial. It is only necessary, then, for the method of projections, to select those lines which require the simplest construction; and for this reason, in descriptive geometry, the position of the plane is indicated by the two straight lines in which it cuts the planes of projection.

Definition: The two straight lines which are the intersection of any plane with the planes of projection are called the traces of that plane. . . .

Conical surfaces similarly have two principle generators. One can firstly regard them as produced by a line of indefinite length which, being subject to passing through a given point, is placed such that it supports itself constantly on a given curve which guides it in its movement. The unique point through which the line passes is the centre of the surface; it is improperly called the apex. In this generation the generating line is again constant in form; it is always a straight line.

One can also produce conical surfaces in another way which, for greater simplicity, we will apply here only to those which have circular bases. These surfaces can be regarded as the paths of the circumference of a circle placed with its plane always parallel to itself and with its centre always on the line running to the apex, its radius in each instant of movement being proportional to the distance of its centre from the apex. . . . In this second generation, not only does the circle circumference, which is the surface generator, change position, but it changes its form at each instant of movement since it changes its radius and, so, its curvature. . . .

When the generations of two curved surfaces are completely determinate and known, when for neither of them is there anything left arbitrary respecting the succession of all the points in space through which they pass, when for each of these points, one of the two projections being taken at pleasure, the other projection can always be constructed; then, if the two surfaces have any common points in space, the position of all such common points is absolutely determinate. It depends both upon the form of the two curved surfaces and upon their respective positions, and is of such a nature that it can always be deduced from the definition of the generations of the surfaces, of which it is a necessary consequence.

The succession of all the points common to two determinate curved surfaces forms generally a certain curved line in space. . . . which in the general case is what is called a curve of double curvature, because it usually participates in the curvature of the two surfaces, on each of which it is situated at the same time, and of which it is the common intersection.

In order to impart greater clarity to the explanation of this method we shall not present it at once with all the elegance of which it is susceptible, but arrive at this by degrees. Moreover, the enunciation will be general and applicable to any two surfaces whatsoever; and although the letters employed will refer to Fig. 26,* which presents the particular

* Fig. 43 in this book.

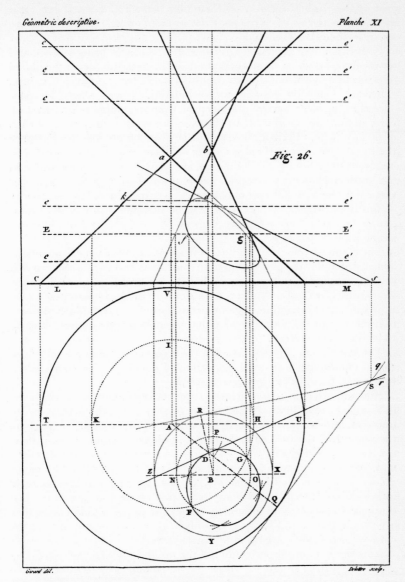

Fig. 43. Plate XI from Monge's *Géométrie descriptive*, 1795. In the main this shows the method used today for determining the curve of intersection of two cones. The drawing appears more complicated as Monge also used it to demonstrate how to draw the projections of a line tangent to this curve at a given point.

case of two conical surfaces with circular bases and vertical axes, it is nevertheless to be conceived that the surfaces under consideration can either of them be other than conical.

Problem 20. The generation of two curved surfaces being known, and all the data which fix these generations being determinate on the planes of projection, construct the projections of the curve of double curvature.

Solution. Conceive a succession of indefinite planes placed in space according to some agreed manner; for example, suppose first that all these planes are horizontal. In this case the vertical projection of each of them will be a horizontal straight line of indefinite length; and since the distances between them are quite arbitrary, suppose as many horizontal straight lines *ee'*, *ee'*, *ee'* &c. as you please to have been drawn in the vertical plane of projection, and this set of straight lines to be the vertical projection of the set of planes we have imagined. Having arrived at this point, the same operation is to be carried out for each of these planes *ee'* which here we proceed to point out for that particular one which is projected as *EE'*.

The plane *EE'* cuts the first surface in a certain curve which can always be constructed if the generation of the surface is known; for this curve is the succession of the points in which the plane *EE'* is pierced by the generating line in all its different positions. Lying in a horizontal plane, it will have its horizontal projection equal, similar and similarly situated to itself; this projection, therefore, can be constructed; suppose it, then, to be the curve *FGHIK*.

The same plane *EE'* will also cut the second surface in another horizontal curve, the horizontal projection of which can be constructed; suppose it, then, to be the curve *FGOPN*.

Now the two curves in which the same plane *EE'* cuts respectively the two surfaces may intersect each other or they may not; if they do not intersect, however far produced, this will be a proof that at the height of the plane *EE'* the two surfaces have no point in common; but if these two curves do intersect, they will do so in a certain number of points, which will be common to the two surfaces and will so be some of the points of the required intersection. In fact, inasmuch as the points of intersection of the two curves are in the first curve, they are in the first of the two surfaces; and inasmuch as they are in the second curve, they are also in the second surface; inasmuch, then, as they are in both the curves at once, they are also in both surfaces.

Now the horizontal projections of the points in which the two curves intersect must be situated both on the horizontal projection of the first and on that of the second; consequently *F*, *G*, &c., the points of intersection of the curves *FGHIK* and *FGOPN*, will be the horizontal projections of so many points in the required intersection of the two curved surfaces. To obtain the vertical projections of the same points, it is to be observed that these points are all comprised in the horizontal plane *EE'*, and that their vertical projections must be situated on the line EE'. If, therefore, the points F, G, &c. be projected to f, g, &c. upon EE' the vertical projection of these points will be obtained.

If the same process be carried out for all the other horizontals ee', ee', &c. as for EE', there will be found for each of them a succession of new points F, G, &c. in the horizontal plane of projection, and in the vertical plane of each projection a succession of new points f, g, &c. Then if a smooth curve be made to pass through all the points F, &c., another smooth curve through all the points G, &c., and so on, the assemblage of all these curves, which may sometimes run one into the other, will be the horizontal projection of the intersection of the two surfaces; and in the same way, if a smooth curve be made to pass through all the points f, &c., another smooth curve through all the points g, &c., and so on, then the assemblage of all these curves, which may sometimes run into one another, will be the vertical projection of the required intersection.

The method which we have just explained is general, supposing a succession of horizontal planes to have been selected for the system of cutting planes. It is, however, to be observed that in certain cases the choice of the system of cutting planes is not a matter of indifference; that such a choice may sometimes be made as to render more simple and elegant the resulting constructions; and that it may even be advantageous perhaps to use, instead of a system of planes, a succession of curved surfaces, which differ from each other only in one of their dimensions. . . .

These passages summarise fairly completely the second part of Monge's descriptive geometry. Long as they are, they represent only a fraction of his complete book. They are, however, worth reading carefully in the light of previous chapters because one can see the influence of many earlier ideas showing through. The relationship with three-dimensional co-ordinate geometry is quite apparent and even the intersecting cones have connections with the method of figured plans. For instance, in the latter system the two cones could be represented as shown at the bottom of Fig. 44, that is, as a series of contour lines on 'mountains' of regular form. The curve of intersection is readily discernible since it is marked by the abrupt kinks in the contour lines. If now we add a front view as shown above, the similarity between this illustration and Monge's version is immediately apparent. In fact, the heavy contour lines are the plane EE' and the circles HIK and $OGNF$ in Monge's plate.

This does not explain the complete generalisation. However, Monge was Minister for Marine at one time in his life and Naval Examiner before this, and one might assume that he came across ship draughts then, if not before. The rib sections in the body plan and the water-lines in the plan are of a similar nature to the contours

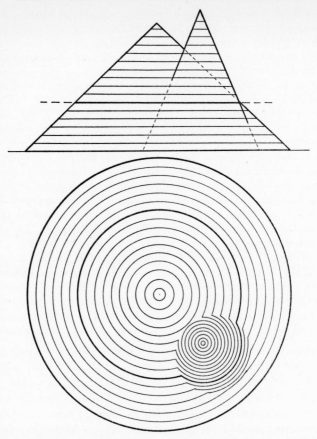

Fig. 44. The two cones of Fig. 43 represented at the bottom by contour lines. The curve of intersection would be the line passing through the 'kinks' in the contours. The upper view has been added so that the whole may be compared with Fig. 43.

of figured plans and, once Monge had started thinking in terms of generation, that is, in relation to movement instead of static forms, he could probably imagine a ship's hull being generated by a curve slowly changing shape as it moved along the length of the hull. Whether this was the case does not matter so long as we, ourselves, see the connection.

Although it does not concern us here, Monge became involved in the French Revolution and was actually a member of the Executive Council* when Louis XVI was executed. Later, in 1793, to-

* This was the group of Ministers acting as a government at the time and who individually signed the death warrant of Louis XVI. Monge became a Minister the day after the throne fell.

gether with a few other scientific men, he exerted himself towards developing the internal resources of France for the supply of the enormous amount of war material which her critical position demanded—she was weakened by the Revolution and threatened by Prussia—and yet which made it difficult to procure. By studying at first hand the various manufacturing processes, Monge not only wrote a number of standard works on making cannon, iron and steel, and gunpowder, but he began to see what was urgently required if France was to become an industrial nation and catch up Britain, where the so-called industrial revolution had been under way for a long time. He became firmly convinced that those concerned with all stages in the production of 'manufactures' should be appropriately educated.

Antoine Laurent Lavoisier, the famous chemist, was one of the scientific men working with Monge at this period, and he also had plans for a scheme of national education. Lavoisier unfortunately went to the guillotine early in 1794, but Monge and his colleagues, Carnot, Prieur and Fourcrey, pressed for action. These academics were acclaimed for the wonderful work they had done in helping to save the nation – possibly the first positive occasion when science had been called in by a government*–and they, and consequently their ideas, were in favour. As a result an Act was passed and late in 1794 the École Normale was formed. This was essentially a training school for teachers, the idea being that if teachers were first produced with the right sort of education they could then spread their knowledge over the country.

The school's curriculum included many 'liberal' subjects, as we should say today, but a large part of the instruction was centred upon combining the theoretical and the practical to give a technical education suitable for those engaged on manufactures. As Monge could see that technical drawing would play an increasingly large part in design, he naturally asked that the ban on his descriptive geometry should be lifted, and this was done. The technical subjects listed as part of the École Normale's tuition were Mathematics, Descriptive Geometry, Physics and Chemistry, but these headings should not be interpreted entirely with today's meanings. Under the heading Descriptive Geometry was also added Applications of Descriptive Geometry, and this not only covered certain aspects of stone-cutting and carpentry, but dealt with the principles of machines and much which today we should class as mechanics.

* The 'government' here was the Committee of Public Safety headed by Robespierre.

Monge's general feelings in this direction are recorded in the preface to his book, thus:

In order to raise the French nation from that position of dependence on foreign industry, in which it has continued to the present time, it is necessary in the first place to direct national education towards an acquaintance with matters which demand exactness, a study which hitherto has been totally neglected; and to accustom the hands of our artificers to the handling of tools of all kinds, which serve to give precision to workmanship and for estimating its different degrees of excellence. . . .

It is necessary in the second place to make popular a recognition of a number of natural phenomena indispensable for the progress of industry, and to exploit, through the advancement of the general instruction of the nation, the fortunate condition in which it finds itself of having at its command the principal resources which are necessary.

Finally, it is necessary to disseminate among our craftsmen the knowledge of the processes used in the crafts and in machines which have for their object either the diminuation of manual labour or the imparting of more uniformity and precision to the results of workmanship; and in this respect it must be admitted that we have much to learn from foreign nations.

All these objectives can only be reached by giving a new direction to national education. This is to be done in the first place by familiarising all young persons of intelligence with descriptive geometry. . . . This art has two principal objects.

The first is to represent with exactness upon drawings which have only two dimensions such objects as have three and which are capable of rigorous definition. From this point of view it is a language necessary to a man of genius, who conceives a project, to those who are obliged to direct its execution, and finally to the craftsmen who are to make the various parts.

The second object of descriptive geometry is to deduce from the exact description of bodies all which necessarily follows from their forms and respective positions. In this sense it is a means of investigating truth; it perpetually offers examples of passing from the known to the unknown; and since it is always applied to objects with the most elementary shapes, it is necessary to introduce it into the plan of national education . . . and make use of this geometry for the representation and determination of the elements of machines by which man, controlling the forces of nature, reserves for himself, so to speak, no other labour in his work but that of his intelligence. [51]

Descriptive geometry did become a key subject in French technical education. It is interesting to note that this probably would not have been the case if Monge had just published a book on the subject. As it was the reverse happened; the subject was injected into

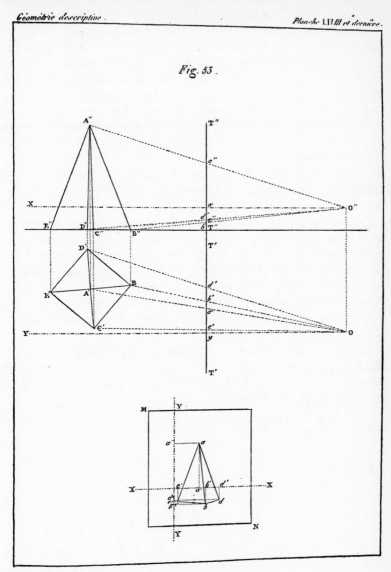

Fig. 53.

Fig. 45. Monge's application of descriptive geometry axioms to perspective projection, added to a late edition of *Géométrie descriptive* after his death. Compare with Fig. 18.

education as the result of historical events and his book followed, it being, in effect, the lectures given at the École Normale.

Monge was called away from the school very soon, however, and he spent many years on scientific work in Italy,* Egypt and Syria, during which time he became a close friend of Napoleon. Under the new regime the school–then reorganised as the École Polytechnique–did not fare very well and Monge was worried over its finances. Napoleon did eventually help after some considerable delay, although the worry had affected Monge considerably. Napoleon's defeat at Moscow hit him hard, as Monge had come almost to hero-worship the Emperor. Worst of all, the return of the monarchy put him 'out of favour' because of his part in the death of Louis XVI. He was cut off from all he cherished and, sadly disillusioned, he died in 1818.

He had published nothing else on descriptive geometry, although later some notes on its application to perspective were found together with a short treatise on shadows, and these were added to a later edition of *Géométrie descriptive* by an ex-pupil, named Brisson. The perspective methods propounded were very similar to what Marolois had proposed in 1629, as can be seen by comparing Fig. 45 with Fig. 18. Monge's work on shadows will be mentioned later in a more appropriate context.

Monge's original work was added to by his assistant J. N. P. Hachette, who wrote *Applications de géométrie descriptive* and *Traité élémentaire des machines*, both of which were based on the subjects taught at the École Polytechnique.

* The treaty signed after the Italian campaign allowed France virtually to plunder Italy of works of art, etc. Monge was sent by Napoleon to Italy, in the first instance, to superintend the collection and renovation of these works, together with a number of painters, sculptors, etc. Leonardo da Vinci's Codex Atlanticus left Milan for Paris in 1796 and Monge probably had a hand in this, even if he was not directly responsible. See Chapter 18.

10

The Nature of Mongean Geometry

ALTHOUGH in the last chapter Gaspard Monge and his descriptive geometry were dealt with at some length, before we move on it is necessary to elaborate his methods and doctrine still further. There are a number of reasons why we have to do this although it tends towards a rather complicated chapter. It was suggested earlier that the significance of Mongean geometry is not easy to assess and that enough information would therefore be given for the reader to make up his own mind. What has been said so far is insufficient for this purpose, in particular because in Britain and America the Mongean content in technical drawing courses has varied very considerably over the last sixty years. A generation ago pure Mongean geometry was taught in a number of higher educational institutions, whereas today drawing instruction is generally much more practically based and many draughtsmen are unaware of Monge's axioms.

What one may have gleaned from the previous chapter will have depended largely upon what one already knows—one might, for instance, read much more into the quotations after having read this complete work—but to summarise we might say that so far we have seen the following. Monge rationalised drawing procedures through showing

(a) that points and lines in space (and therefore bodies bounded by straight edges) could be defined and recorded by giving their projections on to two reference planes at right angles to one another,

(b) that true lengths (and therefore shapes and angles) could be ascertained by revolving any line or face until it was parallel to one of the reference planes,

(c) that curved surfaces could be represented by showing their method of generation, and

(d) that one could define through projections the curves of inter-section of penetrating surfaces.

All of these ideas and some others, such as the development of surfaces, covered by Monge may have been expressed in the last chapter in an unfamiliar way, but their substance is covered in modern engineering graphics irrespective of the source of origin.

Mongean geometry was, however, rather more than this and perhaps the best way to demonstrate this is through an example.

The lectures Monge wrote and which became the substance of his book were devised for students who were destined to become teachers. Now it was Monge's contention that a teacher of a subject should be better informed as to its capabilities than his pupils, and the last part of his book can be considered as a sort of intellectual excursion to demonstrate the versatility of descriptive geometry axioms.

In general terms this last section consists of dealing with a number of three-dimensional problems which are analogous to many well-known two-dimensional constructions. For example, a typical plane geometry problem is to inscribe a circle within a given triangle; the three-dimensional counterpart would then be to inscribe a sphere within a given triangular pyramid. Another simple construction of plane geometry is that of finding the radius and centre of a circle which will pass through three points. The three-dimensional counterpart is to find the centre and radius of a sphere whose surface will pass through four points in space, and it is the solution to this problem which will be demonstrated in this chapter, with a view to showing more clearly the differences between Mongean geometry and drawing methods derived from other sources.

From the initial axioms of descriptive geometry a number of subsidiary rules can be devised and before we tackle the solution to the above problem, it is necessary that we should understand some of these rules and constructions.

We saw earlier that from his work in the field of three-dimensional analytical geometry, Monge introduced the ideas of planes and lines of infinite extent which could be represented on the reference planes by their traces. For instance the plane shown in Fig. 46 (a) would be represented on the reference planes as in (b).

Now if we imagine a line M_1N_1 standing perpendicular to this plane, as in (c), a vertical plane taken through this line will intersect the horizontal plane in a line MN which is the horizontal projection of M_1N_1, and MN is perpendicular to trace XY. Similarly, if we produced a plane through M_1N_1 perpendicular to the vertical plane, we should get a line mn at right angles to trace YZ. In Mongean terms the plane and line normal to it are displayed in (d), and the property of such a line's projections being at right angles to the plane's traces should be noted.

Next, consider a point P_1 on the plane defined by the traces XY,

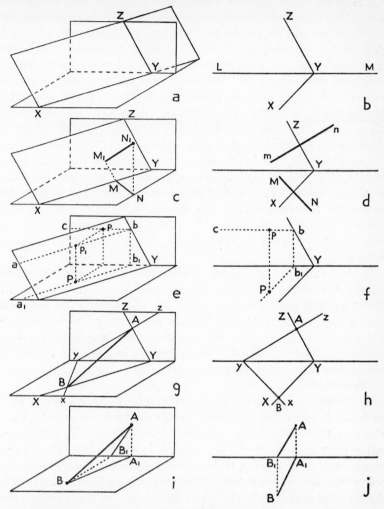

Fig. 46. The axioms of Mongean geometry. The left column shows pictorially the positions of planes, lines and points relative to the planes of projection. The right column exhibits the Mongean methods of depicting these 'in the flat' on a sheet of paper.

(a) and (b) A plane represented by its traces.
(c) and (d) A line normal to a plane represented by its projections.
(e) and (f) A point in a plane represented by its projections.
(g) and (h) A line in space represented by the intersection of two planes.
(i) and (j) A line in space represented by its projections.

YZ, as in (e). If we imagine a horizontal plane through this point, defined by its intersections as abc, then bc will lie in the vertical plane of projection and ab will be projected to the horizontal reference plane as a_1b_1, parallel to XY. The projections of point P_1 will lie on bc and a_1b_1 as p and P respectively, and this is shown in terms of Mongean geometry in (f). This is a useful construction for it can be used to find a missing projection of a point on a plane, given the latter's traces, or for finding a missing trace given the projections of a point on the plane, or for determining a plane parallel to a given plane which passes through a given point.

Two planes in space will, of course, intersect in a straight line, such as AB in Fig. 46 (g). The traces of the two planes will intersect as in (h), and the two points A and B are those where the line AB pierces the reference planes. Finally, this same line in space, AB, can be additionally represented by giving its projections–by dropping A and B onto LM to give points A_1 and B_1. The projections are then AB_1 and A_1B.

If the reader is completely unfamiliar with these Mongean axioms, the above constructions may take a little time to digest. One may be more inclined to make this effort when one has seen how Monge used these constructions to solve a problem, and we will now move on to the particular demonstration problem. The construction for this was not given, in fact, in *Géométrie descriptive*, but Monge recorded the general approach leaving the actual work to the student.

The problem is 'Given four points in space, defined by their projections aA, bB, cC, and dD, to construct the projections of a sphere whose surface will pass through these points'. Since the solution is rather complicated we will deal with it in stages. The solution depends upon the following truism: if one joins any two of the given points by a line in space, and then constructs a plane which bisects the line and is perpendicular to it, this plane will pass through the centre of the required sphere. If one can construct two such planes, they will intersect in a line which passes through the required centre. And if one can construct two such lines in space, their intersection must give the required centre.

Stage one of the solution is given in Fig. 47 (a). One of the points in space is imagined joined by straight lines to the other three and this is represented by joining a to b, c and d, and A to B, C and D in the two projections. Let us consider just one of these lines, ab, AB. We can bisect ab to give point p, the bisecting line produced meeting

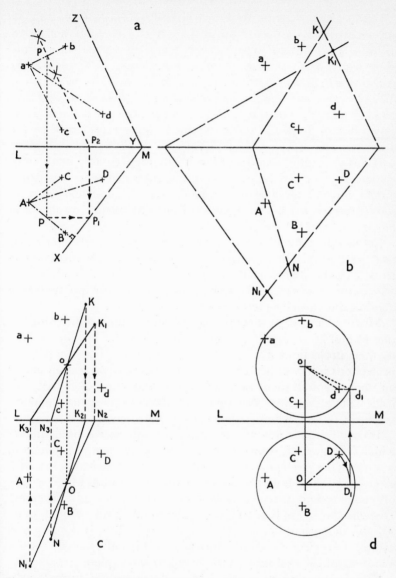

Fig. 47. (a) Stage One: Constructing a plane to bisect a line in space perpendicularly.

(b) Stage Two: Traces of three planes intersecting to define the traces of two lines.

(c) Stage Three: The projections of the two lines derived from their traces to give, by their intersection, the projections of the sphere's centre.

(d) Stage Four: Deriving the sphere's radius.

LM in P_2. The projection of p is, of course, P on AB. Now resorting to the construction shown in Fig. 46 (e) and (f), horizontal and vertical lines from P and P_2 give point P_1 which lies in the trace of the plane which passes through the point p,P. This trace is also at right angles to AB, as shown in Fig. 46 (c) and (d), so it can be drawn as XY. The trace YZ can also be drawn since it passes through Y and is parallel to pP_2. The traces XY, YZ in consequence define a plane which bisects perpendicularly the line in space represented by the projections ab, AB.

If this procedure is adopted for the lines represented by the projections ac, AC, and ad, AD, two other planes in space are determined, and all three of these planes pass through the centre of the required sphere. The traces of these three planes are shown in Fig. 47 (b) and we are now at the second stage.

Let us take these planes in pairs. Two pairs of traces intersect in points K and N. These two points represent where the line of intersection of the planes pierces the reference planes. Similarly the other pair intersect at K_1 and N_1, which are two points where another line in space pierces the reference planes.

Moving on to stage three in Fig. 47 (c), which uses the construction of Fig. 46 (i) and (j), these two lines in space are represented by their projections K_1K_3, N_1N_2 and KN_3, NK_2. The two pairs of projections intersect in o on the vertical plane of projection and O on the horizontal plane of projection. O and o are, of course, projectionally in line since they represent one point in space, the point required, in fact, which is the centre of the sphere.

It only remains now to find the radius of the required sphere, which is stage four, shown in Fig. 47 (d). If the centre is joined to any one of the given points in the two projections, such as shown with od and OD, these lines are the projections of a radius and it is only necessary to find its true length. This is accomplished by revolving D about O to D_1 so that OD_1 is parallel to LM, projecting D_1 to d_1, dd_1 also being parallel to LM, and joining od_1; od_1 is the required radius. Two circles are then drawn with this radius about centres o and O, and the solution to the problem is complete.

This is only one example of Mongean geometry in use but it serves very well to display its essential nature—a doctrine which would allow virtually any three-dimensional problem to be solved on paper in terms of projections and traces.

The reactions to this problem and its solution will undoubtedly be different for various types of readers, but if one has no previous knowledge of this kind of geometry one's reactions may well be very similar to those of other intelligent persons of the 19th century. First, the whole business is a little complicated and needs digesting; second, having become conversant with the methods one comes to recognise what a beautiful, elegant doctrine this is, and one is inclined to have a grudging admiration for Monge; if one is the academic type, one may thirdly wonder how this can be developed for its own sake, just to see what turns up; if one is, on the other hand, a practical man, one may well wonder whether this doctrine, beautiful as it is, has any practical use. Who wants to find the centre of a sphere which will pass through four points in space?

However, we had best leave descriptive geometry for the moment to see what happened elsewhere in this period.

11

Farish: Isometrical Perspective

MONGE'S descriptive geometry was launched as a key element of the instruction given to the students of the École Normale and later those of the École Polytechnique. Besides the subject in its academic form, this was extended into lessons under the heading of Applications of Descriptive Geometry, which not only embraced carpentry and stone-cutting drawing methods (referred to in the 17th and 18th centuries as stereotomie) but also included instruction on the design of machines. In other words Monge's efforts resulted not only in a system of drawing suitable for engineering, but it went a long way towards introducing general courses of engineering study. There being nothing comparable in Europe, Monge's drawing doctrine and the polytechnic school idea spread quite quickly over the Continent.

The story with respect to Britain, America and consequently for the whole English-speaking world was rather different. This will be followed in more detail in a later chapter, but for the moment we will turn to an Englishman, the Reverend William Farish, a contemporary of Monge. There is no counterpart to Gaspard Monge in the English-speaking world, but there are some resemblances between Farish and Monge–both have their names coupled with drawing systems and both were the instigators of courses of engineering instruction.

Farish was born in 1759. He studied at Cambridge University and continued there as a lecturer. He was a brilliant mathematician with general scientific interests, ranging from chemistry to mechanics. After one unsuccessful attempt he eventually secured the post of Professor of Chemistry. However, at the time he gained this position, another professor was already delivering a series of lectures on chemistry and Farish saw no sense in duplicating these. Instead he drew up a *Plan of a Course of Lectures on Arts and Manufactures, more particularly such as relate to Chemistry* which were published in four volumes dated respectively 1796, 1803, 1813, 1821. These books all follow the same pattern, except that each extends and amplifies what was written in the former.

The course of lectures was divided into four parts: Part 1, Metals and Minerals; Part 2, Animal and Vegetable Substances; Part 3, On the Construction of Machines; and Part 4 which dealt with many miscellaneous matters more or less concerned with hydraulics and civil engineering. The last two parts are now considered to be the beginning of engineering education at Cambridge University. So far as can be gathered, the instruction consisted entirely of lectures with demonstration equipment; drawing and design played no part. Nevertheless, a very well-known and useful method of drawing did arise indirectly from these lectures – the familiar isometric projection known to, if not practised by, all draughtsmen.

It is doubtful whether Farish actually 'invented' isometric projection – it probably existed in an empirical form among, for example, engravers – but he was almost certainly the first to investigate the properties of this method of drawing. William Farish became Jacksonian Professor of Natural Philosophy in 1813, and when the Cambridge Philosophical Society was formed he became its first President. As President he delivered the inaugural lectures to the Society, and it is upon these that we can draw for information.

Whilst delivering his engineering lectures, in trying to impress on his students the basic mechanical motions, Farish devised a sort of 'meccano' set – but we might just as well hear about this in his own words:

In the course of Lectures which I deliver in the University of Cambridge, I exhibit models of almost all the more important machines which are in use in the manufactures of Britain.

The number of these is so large, that had each of them been permanent and separate, on a scale requisite to make them work, and to explain them to my audience, I should independently of other objections, have found it difficult to have procured a warehouse large enough to contain them. I procured therefore an apparatus, consisting of what may be called a system of the first principles of machinery; that is, separate parts, of which machines consist. These are made chiefly of metal, so strong that they may be sufficient to perform even heavy work; and so adapted to each other, that they may be put together at pleasure, in every form, which the particular occasion requires.

These parts are various; such as, loose brass wheels, the teeth of which all fit into one another; axes, of various lengths, on any part of which the wheel required may be fixed; bars, clamps, and frames; and whatever else might be necessary to build up the particular machines which are wanted for one lecture. These models may be taken down, and the parts built up again in a different form, for the Lecture of the following day.

As these machines, thus constructed for a temporary purpose, have no permanent existence in themselves, it became necessary to make an accurate representation of them on paper, by which my assistants might know how to put them together, without the necessity of my continual superintendence. This might have been done by giving three orthographic plans of each; one on the horizontal plane, and two on vertical planes at right angles to each other. But such a method, though in some degree in use amongst artists, would be liable to great objections. It would be unintelligible to an inexperienced eye; and even to an artist, it shews but very imperfectly that which is most essential, the connection of the different parts of the engine with one another; though it has the advantage of exhibiting the lines parallel to the planes, on which the orthographic projections are taken, on a perfect scale. This will be easily understood by supposing a cube to be the object represented. The ground plan would be a square representing both the upper and lower surfaces. And the two elevations would also be squares on two vertical planes, parallel to the other sides of the cube. The artist would have exhibited to him three squares; and he would have to discover how to put them together in the form of a cube, from the circumstance of there being two elevations and a ground plan. This method, therefore, giving so little assistance on so essential a point, I thought unsatisfactory. . . .*

Here Farish is giving, very simply, a case which has been presented time and time again right up to today—that whilst multiplane orthographic views are essential for design purposes and are the only realistic way in which shape can be recorded for engineering purposes, the interpretation of such drawings, in which one object is represented by a number of pictures, is a difficult matter, sometimes even for those with considerable experience.

The kind of perspective, which is the subject of this paper. . . . I found much better adapted to the exhibition of machinery; I therefore determined to adopt it and set myself to investigate its principles and to consider how it might most easily be brought into practice.

It is preferable to the common perspective on many accounts, for such purposes. It is much easier and simpler in its principles. It is also, by the help of a common drawing-table and two rulers, incomparably more easy and, consequently, more accurate in its application; insomuch that there is no difficulty in giving an almost perfectly correct representation of any object adapted to this perspective, to which the artist has access, if he has a simple knowledge of its principles, and a little practice.

It further represents the straight lines, which lie in the three principal directions, all on the same scale. The right angles contained by such lines are always represented either by angles of 60 degrees or the supplement

* The more serious reader might note the particular terms used by Farish, such as 'ground plan', 'three orthographic plans', etc., as they have some significance.

of 60 degrees. And this, though it might look like an objection, will appear to be none on the first sight of a drawing on these principles, by any person who has ever looked at a picture. For he cannot for a moment have a doubt that the angle represented is a right angle, on inspection. . . .

Fig. 48 shows some of Farish's mechanical apparatus rigged to demonstrate certain transmission principles. This is based on an

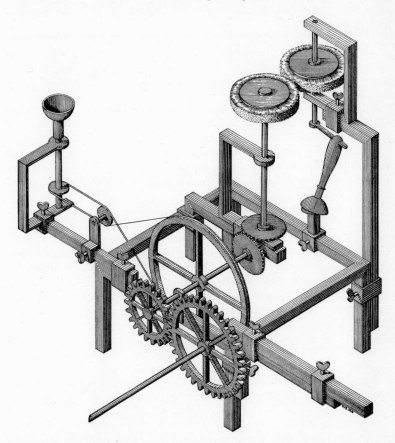

Fig. 48. Plate 2 from Farish's *Isometrical Perspective* 1820. It shows in isometric projection some of the demonstration apparatus assembled to illustrate power transmission principles.

engraving which illustrated his paper; it is drawn, of course, in his famous 'isometrical perspective'. Today, we would class this as a form of one plane orthographic projection and not as any breed of perspective projection. The term 'perspective' was often used very loosely around 1800 to describe any drawing which had a 'picture' look about it; indeed, some orthographic elevations of this period were described as 'in perspective' when they were finished in water colours with shade and shadow to give them a 'solid' appearance. Farish, however, had other reasons for using this term; he considered that an orthographic view was no more than a perspective view with the eye at an infinite distance when the conical visual rays would be parallel.

The principles of this perspective which, from the peculiar circumstance of its exhibiting the lines in the three principal dimensions, on the same scale, I denominate 'Isometrical', will be understood from the following detail:

Suppose a cube to be the object represented. The eye placed in the diagonal of the cube produced. The paper, on which the drawing is to be made to be perpendicular to that diagonal, between the eye and the object, at a due proportional distance from each, according to the scale required. Let the distance of the eye, and consequently that of the paper, be indefinitely increased, so that the size of the object may be inconsiderable in respect of it.

It is manifest, that all the lines drawn from any points of the object to the eye, may be considered as perpendicular to the picture which becomes, therefore, a species of orthographic projection. It is manifest, the projection will have for its outline an equiangular and equilateral hexagon, with two vertical sides, and an angle at the top and bottom. The other three lines will be radii drawn from the center to the lowest angle, and to the alternate angles; and all these lines and sides will be equal to each other, both in the object and representation; and if any other lines parallel to any of the three radii should exist in the object, and be represented in the picture, their representations will bear to one another, and to the rest of the sides of the cube, the same proportion which the lines represented bear to one another in the object.

In models and machines most of the lines are actually in the three directions parallel to the sides of a cube, properly placed on the object. . . .

Fig. 49 is another plate taken from Farish's paper on isometric drawing. His *Fig. 2* shows the isometric cube referred to above, while his *Fig. 3* demonstrates how circles on all the cube's faces, and so circles in the three principal planes, take on a standard shape – a very useful property when considering the illustration of engineering items in which circles play so large a part. His *Fig. 1* shows the top of a 'drawing-table' and, to the right, his drawing rules. To the left, one of these rules has been drawn isometrically to show the shapes of the underside slots, while above this is an isometric

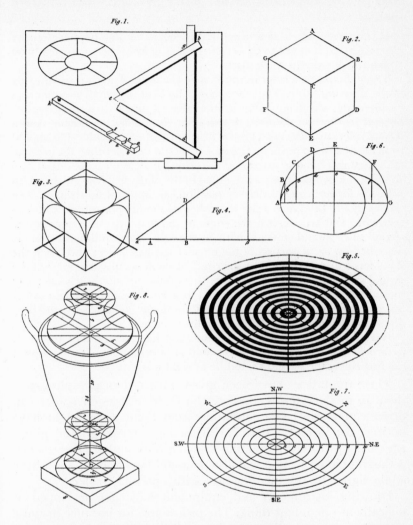

Fig. 49. Plate 1 from Farish's *Isometrical Perspective* 1820. His figs. are: 1, Drawing board, T-square and special 30 degree ruler; 2, The isometric cube; 3, Orientation of ellipses representing circles; 4, Scale for determining ellipse axes lengths; 5, Template to be used for tracing isometric ellipses; 6, Construction for an isometric ellipse; 7, Compass bearings and scale for isometric maps; 8, Isometric construction lines for an urn.

view of two concentric circles joined by eight equally spaced spokes.

It is unnecessary to describe the drawing table any further than by observing that it ought to be so contrived as to keep the paper steady on which the drawing is to be made.

There should be a ruler in the form of the letter T to slide on one side of the drawing table. The ruler should be kept, by small prominences on the under side from being in immediate contact with the paper, to prevent its blotting the fresh drawn lines, as it slides over them. And a second ruler, by means of a groove near one end on its under side, should be made to slide on the first. The groove should be wider than the breadth of the first ruler and so fitted that the second may at pleasure be put into either of the two positions represented in the plate, fig. 1, so as to contain with the former ruler, in either position, an angle of 60 degrees. The groove should be of such a size that when its shoulders a and d are in contact with, and rest against the edges of the first ruler, the edge of the second ruler should coincide with de, the side of an equilateral triangle described on dg, a portion of the edge of the first ruler; and when the shoulders b and c rest against the edges of the first ruler, the edge of the second should lie along ge, the other side of the equilateral triangle. The second ruler should have a little foot at k for the same purpose as the prominences on the first ruler, and both of them should have their edges divided into inches, and tenths or eights of inches.

It would be convenient if the second ruler had also another groove rs, so formed that when the shoulders r and s are in contact with the edge of the first ruler, the second should be at angles to it.

These quotations have been given, rather than paraphrases of them in modern terms, because the really interested reader can prize a great deal of information from them. One might have noticed, for instance, that Farish used the term 'ground plan', which stems from the building drawing philosophy. His views on orthographic projection will also be useful later. Let us, for a little while digress by commenting on Farish's peculiar 'rulers'.

Drawing instruments and equipment have not developed as logically as one might think. The protractor, for instance, is quite a modern device in drawing, for until dividing engines were invented there was no readily available means of making them, at least not very accurately or cheaply. Another familiar accessory which has only been used by draughtsmen generally since about 1850 is the triangular set-square. This is such a simple, obvious instrument that its arrival so late may seem strange. Drawing procedure was not however always as it is today. The main instruments in use from ancient times were the compass and the straight edge. These were, in fact, the only instruments needed in Euclidean Geometry. Compasses were originally dividers used to scratch the vellum or paper, the scratches being inked in later with a quill pen. Compasses were adapted to receive pencil leads about the middle of the 18th century and the ruling pen with blades appeared about that time too.

When modern engineering started – and this was tied up in many ways with building – the drawing board as such came into use with the T-square, which was used generally from the left edge of the board and from the bottom edge to produce lines at right angles; even in the 1830s students were warned to use only these two edges and not to trust the other two. Although it had become more or less standard practice to define engineering objects and arrangements in terms of plans and elevations, these were often drawn on separate sheets and sometimes to different scales. Dimensions were carried from view to view by dividers – when different scales were in use, by proportional dividers.

The square, in its two-bladed form, was in use by carpenters and stone-cutters and sometimes this was used by draughtsmen. When Farish wanted to produce a large number of lines sloping at 30 degrees there was no readily available equipment, hence his postulating the ruler with an inclined slot to move on the T-square. It is interesting to note that Thomas Bradley, in his book *Practical Geometry* published in 1836, gave long descriptions of the drawing equipment then in use, each item fully illustrated, and never once does the triangular set-square appear. He lists compasses and dividers, hair dividers, triangle compasses, beam compasses, proportional compasses, squared boards, T-squares, T-squares with movable blades, parallel rules, lines of chords, protractors, pentographs, centrolineads, and elliptographs – but no triangle. However, by 1860 students could buy triangular set-squares for only a few pence each, for by then the practice of using a T-square only against the left edge of a board and a triangle for vertical lines had superseded the older methods. Whilst it is unprovable, it seems likely that the use of Farish's isometric drawing was directly responsible for the introduction of the triangular set-square, although the practice of using shadows on technical drawings, as we shall see later, probably also had a bearing.

Professor Farish extended his treatise on isometric drawing over two lectures to the Philosophical Society, and in these his enthusiasm was such that he suggested using isometrical perspective for making picture maps, for depicting crystals, Grecian vases and much else. Finally he concluded with:

> The point, however, on which the writer of this paper can speak with the greatest confidence, is on the representation of machines and philosophical instruments; having been himself so much in the habit of practically applying to them the principles that have been detailed.

> The correct exhibition of objects would be much facilitated by the use of this perspective, even in the hands of a person who is but little acquainted with the art of drawing; and the information given by such drawings is much more definite and precise, than that obtained by the usual methods and better fitted to direct a workman in execution.[32]

It is worth comparing to some extent Farish with Monge, particularly to note the differences. Whilst Monge had been a draughtsman and knew quite a lot about designing and manufacturing things, Farish was an academic and seems to have been concerned with assembling things which were already made or were familiar enough to be brought into existence by someone else, the craftsman. Where machines and mechanisms were concerned, Farish's interests lay entirely in their mechanics, the broad scientific principles. It is doubtful whether he understood the concept of accuracy as Monge did; and, of course, being only concerned with broad principles, drawing did not find a place in his engineering lectures – quite the reverse of Monge's curriculum in which drawing was the key subject. This was all a long while ago, yet these two men set two trends, one in England and one on the Continent, which are still with us today. Until quite recent times no British academic institution ever got down to studying the problems of shaping materials or the problems of the design of the machine tools which do this shaping ; this and all detail and production design was left to persons trained within industry.

If Farish had been more practically minded and had put as much effort into propagating his isometrical perspective as Monge had put into his descriptive geometry, isometric drawing might have played a much larger part in engineering than it does. As it was, it languished for some years hidden in the *Cambridge Philosophical Society Transactions*. In 1835 the *British Cyclopedia* was published and this, being based on the written works of the day, devoted a large number of pages to isometric projection, and it may have done much to bring the system into the public eye.

Practical Geometry was published a year later, in 1836, and Thomas Bradley devoted four pages – out of some hundreds – to isometric drawing. The general construction he gives is of some interest as it tends to demonstrate the then academic approach to the geometry of drawing. Referring to Fig. 50:

Let *ab* be given as the side of an original square, bisect it in *p* by a perpendicular to it; make *px* equal to *pa* or *pb*; then set off the length of the diagonal *ax*, each way from *p*, along *ab* produced to *d* and *f*; from *d* or *f*, with *df* for a radius, describe a segment of a circle, and from *f* or *d*, with the same radius, intersect it in *y* and *z*; bisect the arcs *fy*, *fz*, by lines from *d* which will cut *px* in *e* and *c*; then *fe*, *fc* being drawn, they will complete the projection of the square. Lines through *a* and *b* parallel to the sides will give the extremities of the minor axis of the inscribed ellipse and *ab* will be the major.

This quotation is useful, especially when compared with later work in axonometric projection, in demonstrating how the 19th-century academics felt obliged to reduce everything geometrical to the axioms of Euclid. It also exhibits a stage further than Farish took the subject. In Farish's paper, an edge of one unit in the object was drawn as one unit in the picture. Undoubtedly he realised that in truth the line on the drawing should be foreshortened, but he did not bother over this for a number of reasons. The first was that it was part of the simplicity of the system that measurements could be made along isometric axes with an ordinary rule. The second was that in producing drawings of his

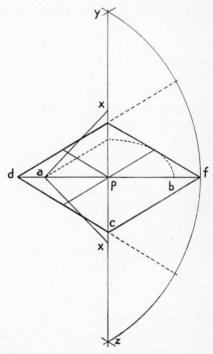

Fig. 50. Bradley's interpretation of isometric in terms of Euclidean Geometry from *Practical Geometry* 1836.

'machines' he used a scale of 1 to 8 reduction; since this was an arbitrary ratio which made the representations bear no resemblance in size to the original objects, there was not much point in introducing another overall reduction such as would happen by correcting dimensions for foreshortening. Bradley's construction, however, is based on true size projection and the sides of his rhombus representing a square are not true size, but suitably foreshortened. Notice, however, that the given true size of the square's edges, *ab*, is also the size of the major axis of the inscribing ellipse of the rhombus. In Farish's method where true sizes are used for the rhombus edges, the whole shape is scaled up, and the major axis of the inscribing ellipse is larger than true size. His *Fig. 4* (in Fig. 49) is a simple proportional device through which the lengths of ellipse axes may be found.

In 1851 J. F. Heather of the Royal Military Academy, Woolwich, prepared a book called *An Elementary Treatise on Descriptive Geometry*, which was a straight translation of various parts of Monge's book considered by him to contain the essentials. To round off the work, he added a last section on isometric projection and here we see for the first time the modern method of isometric drawing using set-squares and an isometric scale.

Isometric drawing was taken up mainly in architectural and building drawing–beams, planking, brickwork and such like being peculiarly suitable for isometric representation because of the inherent 'squareness' of these items and building in general.

In engineering, isometric drawing has played little part really, at least in Britain where it originated, although strangely enough educationalists have always taught it and no engineering drawing-book has ever appeared without expounding the technique.

Although, in this chapter, we have tended to compare Monge and Farish, and their work in general, it is the differences rather than any similarity which is of most interest. In so far as drawing is concerned we have here the beginnings of an inherent rift–which goes back to a very early chapter when we discussed the nature of drawing. Whilst depicting objects and arrangements through a number of 'true shape' views is necessary to record the shape or arrangement and to allow us to deduce additional information, representing one object by one 'picture' is much easier to interpret. One cannot, as it were, have it both ways.

As in the cases of stereographic and perspective projections, isometric projection has its primary and secondary geometries, derivable from and dependent upon one another. The primary geometry of the isometric projection is exhibited at the top of Fig. 51. This shows a cube in space rotated and tilted until its diagonal lies on a line perpendicular to the picture plane. Space projectors from the corners parallel to one another and normal to the plane pierce the

ISOMETRIC
PRIMARY GEOMETRY

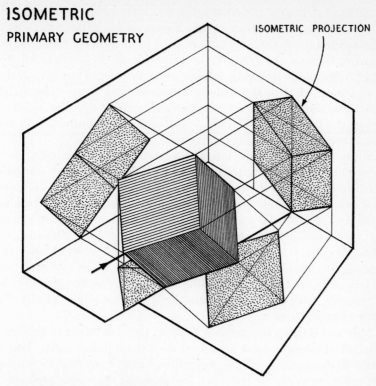

ISOMETRIC PROJECTION

SECONDARY GEOMETRY

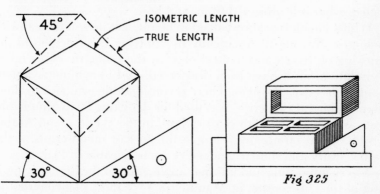

45°

ISOMETRIC LENGTH
TRUE LENGTH

30°   30°

Fig 325

Fig. 51. The primary and secondary geometries of isometric projection. When the 30 degree set-square came into use to facilitate the latter, many persons equated any drawing made with the aid of a set-square to isometric—as bottom right, an example which is really oblique projection.

picture plane to give the outline shown. This outline is reproduced in its true form at the bottom of the Figure and this shows the secondary geometry properties which may be used to make an isometric drawing without resorting to the principle of projection. All the cube's edges are vertical or sloping at 30 degrees. They are all the same length, that is, the scale of foreshortening is the same in all three directions. The foreshortening scale can be deduced by comparing the top face of the cube, exhibited as a rhombus, with the true shape of the square it represents.

Many persons from the late 1800s to the present, including teachers who are not specialists in drawing, only come across isometric drawing in terms of its secondary geometrical properties, and, not even grasping these properly, they come to think that any drawing made with the use of a 30-degree set-square is an isometric drawing. Fig. 325 from *The Workman's Manual of Engineering Drawing*, by John Maxton, is reproduced at the bottom of Fig. 51. Under the heading of Isometric Projection, the author says, 'Almost any variety of such objects, all pleasing to the eye, can be projected, as in Fig. 325, with the T-square and little wooden angle, hardly any measurement being necessary.'

This was written in England in 1871, but a drawing of this kind labelled 'Isometric' still appeared in a book dated 1961. This is really an example of oblique projection, but to heap confusion upon confusion, so many authors then and now use the word 'projected' as in the above quotation, when they mean 'drawn'. If it is projected, what is it projected from, and how?

Whilst Farish is acknowledged to be the first person to deal with isometric drawing systematically by applying its principles to the drawing of diverse mechanical objects, the isometric cube, taken in isolation, must have been discovered, and its symmetry noted, many times over the ages. There is considerable evidence to show that 'empirical isometric' was used for depicting fairly simple objects as early as the 15th century both in the Western and Arabic worlds. There are many examples in Persian manuscripts of the 15th century and similar tendencies are noticeable in Plate 2.

A very interesting and unusual application of the isometric position of the cube occurs in Manuscript C of those of Leonardo da Vinci held in the Library of the Institut de France, Paris. It appears in da Vinci's experiments and notes on the free fall of bodies. As shown in Fig. 52, a cube is imagined falling in three different ways, A, B and C (the letters in the illustration are in Leonardo's 'mirror writing'). At A, the cube is falling with one face flat on to the air. At B, the cube is rotated so that it is falling with two faces forming an edge to cleave its way through the air. At C, the cube is both

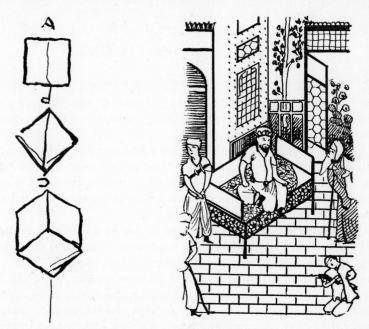

Fig. 52. *Left*: Cubes sketched by Leonardo da Vinci.
   Right: Example of an empirical form of drawing in 15th-century Persian manuscripts, which is isometric in form. (From a Persian MS. in British Museum.)

rotated and tilted so that the axis of the cube is in the line of fall; three faces present a point to cleave through the air. If the direction of fall is taken as the line of sight, the views of the three cubes are, respectively, a square, two adjacent rectangles, and three abutting rhomboids, that is, the form of the 'isometric cube'.

12

The Nineteenth Century in Britain

THE development of engineering drawing—in theory and in practice—is very much more difficult to follow in Britain than on the Continent, although on the practical side there is much common to general progress in other countries.

At the time of Monge and Farish, the Industrial Revolution was well under way and perforce large numbers of technical drawings had had to be produced. Though these drawings had not the logical basis of Monge's descriptive geometry, through necessity they had tended to become fairly conventionalised.

Considering theoretical aspects first, a close look at both drawings and books of the early 19th century suggests that technical drawings were viewed on two, and possibly three, levels. At the craftsman level they were seen more or less as pictures or true shape views. Above this there was the concept of orthographic projection entertained by the scholars. There was possibly an intermediate level—that of the better educated engineer—of which little information is available.

Some idea of the scholar's view of orthographic projection can be gleaned from Farish's words given in the previous chapter. A more direct understanding is displayed in the works of Thomas Bradley, who taught at the Engineering Department of King's College, London. Bradley wrote quite a number of books summarising the geometrical knowledge of the times. In one on projections it is rather significant that out of many hundreds of pages, only nine were devoted to orthographic projection. One reason for this was that, compared with the perspective projection, Bradley thought orthographic projection to be almost self-evident. Perspective seems to have ranked very high with geometers at the end of the 18th century—indeed such was its fascination that quite apart from its utilitarian value it had become a subject for intellectual pursuit. Also Bradley, rather like Farish, considered, or at least asked others to consider, orthographic projection to be perspective with an infinite viewing distance.

If the distance of the vertex from the original object, instead of being at a finite distance as is always supposed in perspective projection, be assumed to be at an infinite distance, the rays from the object, instead of forming a pyramid, will form a prism and will be parallel among one another; and the projection becomes what is called orthographic. . . .

The projections of objects by parallel rays, perpendicular to the plane of projection, are called the plans or elevations of those objects according as the plane is supposed to be horizontal or vertical. . . . The plans and elevations made use of by architects and engineers are really such projections drawn on paper, as if produced from imaginery models. . . .

By a plan or elevation made under such conditions, the dimensions or magnitudes of a rectangular solid which are in one direction, or in planes parallel to the plane of projection, can only be represented; to convey any idea, therefore, of the whole solid, two such projections, at least, on two planes perpendicular to each other are required and these projections being separate figures, cannot convey to the mind at one impression an idea of the form of the object. . . .[14]

Once again we have a geometer's reminder of how difficult it is to build up a mental picture of an object from a number of separate views.

One can tell a lot from omissions, and orthographic projection in principle was considered to be so obvious to Bradley that he did not even bother to illustrate the above by showing a plan or elevation. In fact, most of Bradley's writings on this subject were concerned with making orthographic projections of objects which were *not* parallel to the plane of projection. Two laminal figures treated by Bradley's orthographic projection methods are shown in Fig. 53. In the first, the true shape of a pentagon is given as *CDEFG*. This pentagon is imagined to be lying on an inclined plane, *AH*, with *AB* as the horizontal. The figure is then projected onto the vertical plane *AI*, the result being the figure *cdefg*. As we might expect, the positions of points *cdefg* are found by the intersections of lines drawn from *CDEFG* and *F'D'C'*. Notice that only three points are used on the inclined plane. The figure *cdefg* is completed by using a property we came across in Desargues's projective geometry and earlier in sun-dialling. This is that if two figures are projectionally related, as *cdefg* and *CDEFG* are, then corresponding lines, such as *fg* and *FG* produced, meet on the line which is the intersection of the two planes containing the projections. This property is again made use of in the lower drawing, where the diameter is produced through *F* to *E*, so that *EC* produced is the projection of the diameter on the vertical plane.

Bradley expanded this technique and went so far as to project, in a very laborious way, a dodecahedron with triangular faces—giving what we should today call an axonometric view.

Monge's descriptive geometry was slow in crossing the English Channel and when it did arrive his ideas were slow to spread, possibly because they were on too theoretical a level for the practical Englishman. In 1868 a teacher in Scotland by the name of A. W. Cunningham became greatly disturbed at the apathy in Britain and

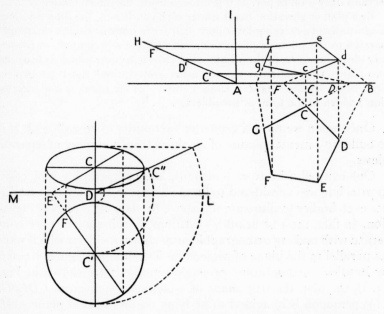

Fig. 53. Bradley's illustrations for orthographic projection, from *Practical Geometry* 1836. In layout and concept these are quite different from those of Mongean geometry. In effect, the process is reversed, apparent shapes being derived from true shapes.

he wrote a pamphlet—nearly of book length—called *Notes on the History, Methods and Technological Importance of Descriptive Geometry.* His feelings are quite apparent from the Prefatory Note.

The following pages have been compiled with the view of directing attention to the importance of the study of Descriptive Geometry. Except in the special schools under the immediate supervision of the Government, the subject appears to be still but little taught in this country, and much ignorance prevails, even amongst teachers, respecting what in France and Germany is considered the very ground-work of Technical

Education. For, as the application of Geometry to the arts is naturally the first point to attract attention in considering the general scheme of Technology, the Géométrie Descriptive of Monge, which affords the means of such application, must form a fundamental branch of Technical Education. That it is still comparatively unknown in this country, I attribute to the fact that Euclid is still the only text-book on the Ancient Geometry in general use. This infatuated adherence to the exclusive use of a work inadequate to the requirements of the age necessarily cramps the development of the science in its Practical departments.[18]

Although this 'pamphlet' was a bit of a tirade it did contain some very useful information, and for the historian it presents an interesting picture of what an intelligent teacher thought of things at the time. Cunningham finished his writings by appending an unusual kind of table on which the diagram below is based.

PRACTICAL GEOMETRY.

THE BASIS OF THE SCHEME OF TECHNOLOGY.

PLANE.	SOLID.	SOLID.
GRAPHICAL, which is also CONSTRUCTIVE.	GRAPHICAL. PROJECTIONS.	CONSTRUCTIVE. MODELS, ETC.

considered as represented by
DESCRIPTIVE GEOMETRY, which is the Theory
of the
ART OF   SHAPING
DRAWING.   MATTER.

SCIENTIFIC predominates in FRANCE.	AESTHETIC predominates in GERMANY.	INDUSTRIAL predominates in GREAT BRITAIN.

This chart, taken together with his text, is meant to suggest that whereas on the Continent there were elegant drawing methods through which all manner of three dimensional problems could be tackled on paper, in Britain one would have to make a model or actually shape a piece of material to find out. In so far as formal education was concerned Cunningham was probably justified in suggesting this, but he failed to give the credit due to craftsmen. Whilst they did not think in terms of high abstractions as Monge did, their knowledge and common sense was sufficient for them to work out suitable practical drawing constructions for most of their problems. These constructions may have been scratched on slate, chalked on a blackboard or drawn actually on the material being worked; they may not have been made on paper or recorded in books, but this is not the same as denying their existence.

Cunningham, no doubt, recognised that craftsmen did make drawings, but his campaign was justified in the sense that he wanted to see systematic drawing education replace the custom where methods were passed on to apprentices by craftsmen, almost secretly, and every method specifically appertaining to a particular trade. He stated that, to his knowledge 23 authors had written on the subject of descriptive geometry in France since Monge's time, 24 in Germany, and that an indeterminate number of books had appeared in Spain, Belgium, Denmark, Sweden, Norway and the u.s.a. Monge's work, he said, had also been translated and published in Egypt and Italy, the latter country being introduced to the subject as early as 1804. He even recorded how a French deserter had given descriptive geometry to the Russians.

It seems that as Mongean geometry had been classed as a military secret in France, as soon as it was published copies were obtained by the British War Office. In due course the subject was taught in British Military Schools. By 1840 Thomas Bradley at last came across the subject and he gave a course of lectures on descriptive geometry at King's College, London. The material for these lectures was taken from the work of a second generation French writer, De Fourcy, and after these lectures an English work, edited by Bradley and Professor T. G. Hall, was published. The book, called *The Elements of Descriptive Geometry*, was as dry as dust and, in retrospect, appears to have been compiled like Euclid, in the form of proposition after proposition without a clue to any of it having a useful purpose.

Although real information is scarce, it seems that the then academics misinterpreted the nature of descriptive geometry. Confronted with new problems and solutions, such as the example we have seen of finding the surface of a sphere to pass through four points in space, they at first imagined that they had a really new geometry in their hands which could be used to extend our knowledge. Cunningham mentioned this as follows:

Now so great was the admiration accorded to descriptive geometry on its first promulgation by Monge, that many were disposed to regard it as a real means of extending the science of geometry. This, however, is not the case. The mistake arose probably from overlooking the fact that a large amount of rational geometry was necessarily mixed up with the exposition of mere descriptive operations; and more particularly from not clearly perceiving that the truths may be deduced from the *Theory* of Projection without any necessity for graphically exhibiting them by the *Methods* of Projection.[18]

Finding eventually that Mongean geometry was a dead end so far as they were concerned, the academics dropped the subject, and it was not until the beginning of the 20th century that we see descriptive geometry accepted as part of higher science education. It might have been taken up more readily if, in more practical courses, an indigenous breed of drawing had not emerged.

This development is part of a very complex story which is better understood by forgetting theoretical aspects for a moment. In the early part of the 19th century most engineering drawings were produced by engineers or craftsmen. By the middle of the century this had changed and there was also a considerable population of draughtsmen. They were not all of a likeness, however. Some were virtually engineers—equivalent to the modern designer-draughtsman; some were production experts, adept at redesigning functional parts for optimum manufacture; but a very much larger group were somewhat equivalent to what we would call tracers, although nevertheless virtually artists. Whilst this was just before the time when blue-prints came into use, engineering had expanded to the stage where single copies of drawings were unrealistic. Besides making copies, these 'artists' made many very finely finished drawings of a type unfamiliar to most of us today. A good example of 1850 is shown in Plate 6, very similar to the 'measured drawings' still made by architectural students.

In 1859 this draughtsman population was large enough for some persons to suggest a Society of Engineering Draughtsmen and the correspondence which ensued in *The Engineer* (London, December 16, 1859, and December 30, 1859) is worth recording.

Sir,

The engineering draughtsmen of the metropolis have been, for some time past, discussing at intervals the propriety of establishing among themselves a society of a scientific and philanthropic character; but there appears somehow to be a want of cohesion in the body, which militates against so desirable a consummation. . . .

I am decidedly of opinion that there exist in London all the elements for the construction of a society of mechanical draughtsmen, and that it requires but determination to unite these elements. That determination, however, appears to be totally wanting. . . .

What, then, are draughtsmen to do? I say–since they cannot apparently form a society of their own–let them join other societies of a nature similar to that they wish to create. There are at least three such societies at present in existence in London, and either of these would open its portals to receive them. Firstly, there is the Society of Engineers, next the Association of Foremen Engineers, and thirdly the Civil and Mechanical Engineers' Society. . . .   J.N.

The writer of this letter pointed out the lack of cohesion amongst draughtsmen but failed to show why; in fact, his idea of draughtsmen being engineers of a kind was only applicable to a minority who had no wish to associate themselves with the 'artist' type of draughtsmen. These sentiments were expressed in another letter published two weeks later.

Sir,

Of mere copyists there are hundreds too many. Although mechanical drawing may be an art by itself, and although an excellent draughtsman may be always sure of employment, the demand for mere drawing is limited, and really excellent draughtsmen have always been scarce. The gentlemanly nature of the employment is attractive, no doubt, and it is to this circumstance that we must attribute the brisk trade of the drawing-instrument and water-colour dealers. Perseverance will do much, but if mere adventurers in drawing, who would be draughtsmen because they would like an easy, irresponsible employment, were to examine a portfolio of really first-class drawings–such as those of 'The Great Eastern' in Mr. Scott Russell's office–they might conclude they were missing their vocation, and determine upon looking up something else in which the probability of success would be more in their favour. A young man with only sufficient capacity to become a third-rate draughtsman should have very moderate wishes, for he can never command either the respect or salary which would satisfy a gentleman. But if there is more in him than a faculty for mere ink marking and colour daubing, let him develope himself by all means. Above all, let him devote himself to the design of mechanism in its simplest forms . . . etc. . . .

In other words, this correspondent pointed out that there was a difference between draughtsmen who could be creative in an engineering sense, and those who were mere copyists.

However, courses of instruction come into being according to the demand, and at this period there was a demand for courses which would teach 'young gentlemen' how to use the pencil, the pen and the brush in the execution of finished engineering drawings. Instruction of this kind borrowed a great deal from existing courses in architectural drawing, and the carry-over of architectural ideas and practice can be seen in many of the old machines produced at this time. The legs of some machines were cast as Doric and Ionic pillars and many a functional bracket had leaf embellishments cast into it. Students were taught to draw 'quatre-foils' and 'cinque-foils' and other ornamental forms and one can hardly blame them for introducing these into their later work.

These courses were, in the main, copying ones and they embraced little of the theory of technical drawing. The reaction, of course, came and this is recorded for us in the preface of a book published in 1857–*An Elementary Treatise on Orthographic Projection, being a new method of teaching the Science of Mechanical Engineering Drawing*, by William Binns.

The great and increasing demand for a knowledge of Geometrical Drawing as applied to the Arts has induced me to lay before the public a course of instruction which I designed in 1846 for the Students of the College for Civil Engineers, Putney, and practised with success until the close of that Institution in 1851. . . .

Having, in the title page of this book, presumed to designate the system here recommended 'a new method of teaching Mechanical and Engineering Drawing', it may be desirable to show wherein the novelty consists, by a comparison with the usual mode of teaching, which, so far as my knowledge extends, is from the 'flat'–that is, from copy–the practice being to lay before each student of the class a drawing of some part or parts of a structure which he is requested to copy. This being done, another drawing, probably more elaborate, is laid before him; and the same course is pursued until he becomes tolerably expert with his instruments and brushes, and eventually is enabled to make a very creditable or even a highly finished drawing from *copy*. If, however, at the end of one or two years' practice the copyist is asked to make an end elevation, side elevation and longitudinal section of his black-lead pencil, or a transverse section of the box containing his instruments, the chances are that he can neither do the one or the other. . . . The remedy in all such cases has been to commence a course of study from the very beginning; and the result has ever been satisfactory . . .

With the conviction that the subject of Orthographic Projection is the ABC of that description of drawing which is universally adopted as a means of representing all kinds of engineering structures, as well as articles in process of manufacture, it has been my sole aim . . . to reduce the subject of Mechanical Drawing to a series of fixed rules and principles methodically arranged; so that the whole subject, from the projection of a point or line to the projection of the most complex object, forms as it were a chain of so many links. . . .[6]

About this time a number of similar books appeared and it will be useful to deal with these as a whole to see the general philosophy. Binns's book became popular and a second course followed in 1869. Both were essentially of use to prospective draughtsmen and engineers. On the other hand another series of books appeared for the workman, industry still being such that a considerable amount of drawing and marking out was in the hands of craftsmen. These books were written by Ellis A. Davidson, a lecturer on Engineering and Architecture in the City of London. A quotation from the preface of the first book on 'Projection' will show how 'down to earth' they were:

In order to fit the course of instruction . . . to adults whose elementary education may be deficient, the author has deemed it best to assume, in the first instance, utter ignorance on the part of pupils. Thus it will be seen in Problem 1, no geometrical terms, such as 'describe an arc', are used, the learner being merely told to place the steel point of his compass on a given spot whilst tracing part of a circle with the pencil leg. . . .[20]

Fig. 54 demonstrates how Davidson introduced the ideas of projections to those with 'utter ignorance'. As with Monge, he showed a horizontal and vertical reference plane, although these were not demonstrated as theoretical planes, but as real ones – two solid boards hinged together and held in the right-angle position by a strut, with a screw for disengaging the strut so that the vertical plane could be laid horizontal. The lower drawing showed what the two boards looked like when opened out flat, i.e. how these lines would be represented in an orthographic drawing. It shows the projection of a vertical line, a horizontal line perpendicular to the vertical plane and a horizontal line parallel to the vertical plane. Adding these together one could then show how to represent a box and from thereon everything could be developed naturally. In a similar way Davidson also demonstrated projection onto the third reference plane, i.e. the side view projected onto a plane perpendicular to both other reference planes.

Binns introduced the idea of projection onto planes by the simple expedient of using the pages of the book itself. The plan of a simplified house was printed on one page and its front view on the other page opposite. These were joined up by projection lines and the reader was asked to lay the book flat and rotate the elevation page until it was in the upright position. A 'house' was then to be imagined standing on the plan and the relationship between this and the two drawn views was established.

PLATE 6

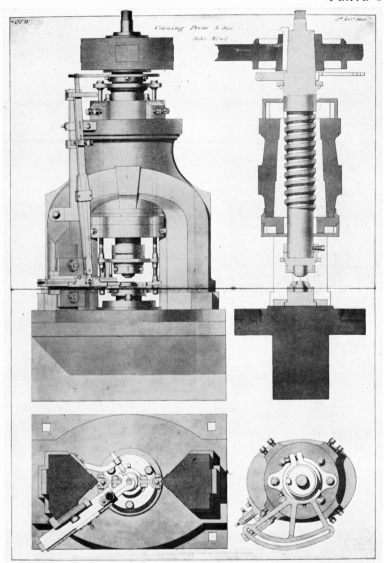

A drawing of a Coining Press for the Soho Mint, dated October 3, 1850. A good example of architectural drawing practice carried over into engineering drawing. The parts are tinted with water colour and shadows are used to give the three-dimensional effect. The draughtsman himself has had some difficulty in interpreting the bare outlines—notice in the sectioned side view that an error was made when colouring the T-section base, and subsequently rectified.

PLATE 7

Draught of a Third-Rate Ship of 1670 taken from Si

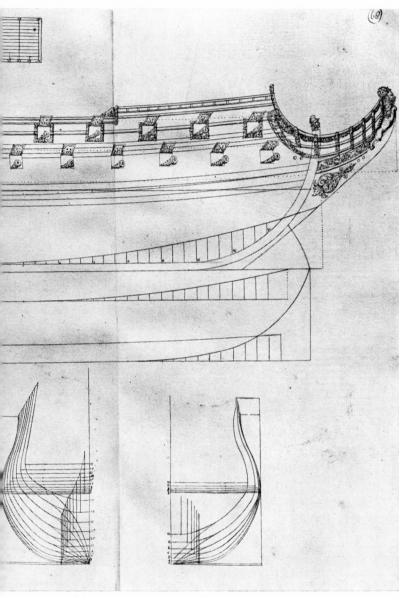

ne's Manuscript 'Doctrine of Naval Architecture'.

PLATE 8

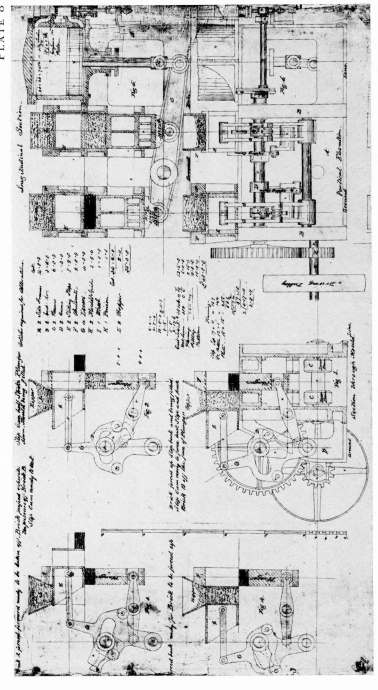

An engineering drawing made in England about 1820 for a brick-making or -moulding machine.

A further step in both Binns's and Davidson's books was the projection of views from 'rotated' plans (or elevations). An example

FIG. I.

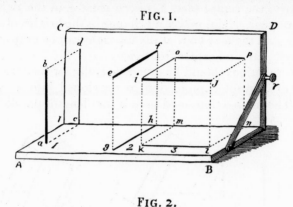

FIG. 2.

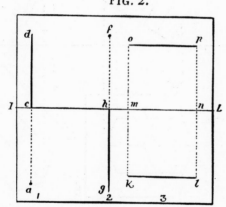

Fig. 54. Davidson's method of introducing orthographic projection to those with 'utter ignorance'.

from Binns is given in Fig. 55. The two views at the left are the front and top views of a hexagonal prism. In the middle the front view of the prism has been tilted on *AB*. The vertical dimensions in the

The plate opposite shows a design layout drawing for a brick-making or moulding machine and it was drawn on heavy hand-made paper with a linen backing. All ferrous parts are shown in light Prussian blue and non-ferrous parts in orange. Notice that the drawing was also used to enter up the calculated weights in cwt, qr and lb, and also the estimated cost of patterns, castings, machining and fitting which have been put in with pen and ink. The drawing was probably made for approval of the scheme, whereupon further more detailed drawings would be required. The drawing was in the possession of the late George Noble.

plan view remain unchanged by this movement, so the new plan can be projected from the original plan and the new tilted front elevation.

Similarly, the centre plan has been rotated in the right views. This movement, again, makes no change in the heights of the front elevation, and the new view at the top right can be projected from the rotated plan and centre front view.

These operations should be noted carefully for they become the basis of orthographic projection as developed into a system of axioms. The main axiom used here is that lengths parallel to pro-

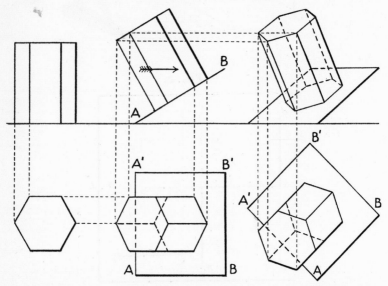

Fig. 55. The foundations of British orthographic projection as exhibited by Binns in *An Elementary Treatise on Orthographic Projection* 1857.

jectors remain unchanged if the 'object' is rotated about an axis parallel to the projectors. For example *AA'* is parallel to the vertical projection lines shown dotted and lengths measured parallel to *AA'* in the plan remain unchanged at whatever angle *AB* may be inclined.

Orthographic projection in this sense, sometimes called solid geometry drawing, became the basis of all British drawing theory, in the same way that descriptive geometry became the basis of continental drawing theory. Fully developed they both accomplish similar ends, but the underlying philosophies are different. Orthographic projection as a science is based on drawing solid objects first, and develops to solve pure spatial problems later. Descriptive geometry, on the other hand, commences with abstractions and later applies these to real objects. When one comes to think of it, what is shown in Fig. 55 is the reverse of Monge's opening thesis. Whereas he started with an inclined line in space and proceeded to find its true length, the British counterpart started with a true shape and proceeded to 'move it around' until all its dimensions appeared foreshortened.

Orthographic projection in this sense has a long natural line of history, as one can see from Fig. 56 which has the date 1527–in

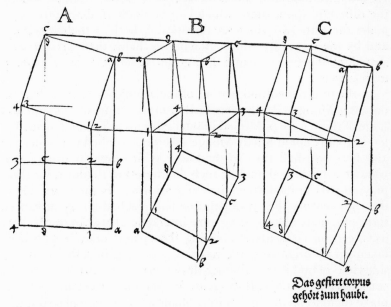

Das gefiert corpus
gehört zum haubt.

Fig. 56. Projections on to the equivalent of first and second auxiliary planes as demonstrated by Dürer in 1525. This stage follows that shown in Fig. 24 and it will be noted that the crate shown is not a cube, its edges being in the proportions 10 : 10 : 8.

fact, it is from Dürer. It is the logical extension of the method Dürer used for his 'crated' heads and the frameworks exhibited in this Figure are not views of a cube, but of a box with sides of ratio 10 : 10 : 8 like the boxes of Figs. 23 and 24.

Over the years, of course, both orthographic projection and descriptive geometry have borrowed much from one another, but both systems could have developed, it seems, in isolation, and the drawing philosophies in Britain and on the Continent of Europe are still noticeably different today because of their different roots.

13

Drawing and Early British Technical Education

In the introduction to *Géométrie descriptive*, Monge said: 'Among the different applications which can be made of descriptive geometry there are two which are remarkable, both by their generality and by the ingenuity which attaches to them; these are the constructions of perspective and the rigorous determination of shadows in drawings'.

In the original edition neither of these subjects were dealt with, but after Monge's death some further manuscripts were found and some of these were published in later editions as a supplement. We have already noted briefly Monge's methods applied to perspective and here we shall turn to shadows. At first sight one may well wonder why there should be such an interest in shadows, for these play no part in modern engineering drawing. By the beginning of the 19th century the art of painting had reached a very advanced state and, there always being some interaction between similar subjects, certain elements of painting theory and practice had been taken up by architects. We have already seen that the front and side views of buildings, although drawn to scale, were still essentially considered as pictures. It was natural, therefore, to colour them and make them as lifelike as possible. Shadows were then placed under balconies, by the sides of buttresses and chimney-stacks and so on. They helped create the general three-dimensional impression of the objects depicted.

Monge tried to put this, like most other aspects of drawing, on a sound basis.

It has been stated that descriptive geometry must be regarded from two points of view. Under the first, it is to be considered as a means of research for arriving with precision at certain desired results; and it is thus employed in stone-cutting and carpentry. Under the second, it is simply a means of representing objects and, in this case, the determination of shadows is an auxiliary advantage of it.

Persons conversant with the methods of this science are aware that a single projection does not suffice to define an object; and that two projections are necessary; because on a plane one of the dimensions is always wanting, but by means of two projections the three dimensions are determined. In examining then the description of an object completely given by means of its two projections, the horizontal projection must be compared with the vertical projection and it is from this incessant comparison that the knowledge of the form of the proposed object is deduced.

Although the method of projection is simple and possesses a peculiar kind of elegance, yet the obligation of comparing incessantly two projections one with the other is a trouble which can be considerably diminished by the employment of shadows.

Suppose for instance that we have a horizontal projection containing all the dimensions in length and breadth, but which determines nothing respecting the dimensions in height; if the bodies be considered to be illuminated in a known manner (and it is convenient to adopt, in general, the most natural manner, that with which we are most familiar) for example by parallel rays of light, these bodies will be throwing shadows on one another and on the horizontal plane above which they are placed, and by means of the extent and form of these shadows we can immediately judge of the vertical dimensions. Thus the direction of the rays of light being known, there is no need of two projections; one only with the traces of the shadows will give a complete idea of the object under consideration; and if we have both the horizontal and vertical projections with the shadows constructed, these two projections will be more easy to read, and will show the object more readily than if we only had the bare projections without shadows.[52]

The first part of this quotation is another admission that multiview orthographic drawings are easy to make and are a record, but can be very difficult to interpret. As one can imagine, rather like figured plans, one-plane representation with but shadows added was only successful where very simple objects were represented – and engineering objects, at any rate, tended to become more and more complex. Nevertheless the addition of shadows as an aid in interpretation was used for some time quite extensively – even in the early 1900s the use of shadows in engineering drawing was still taught and examined in Britain, although they had by then largely gone out of use in industry.

An example of the auxiliary use of shadows has already been given in Plate 6 – a drawing of a coining press dated 1850. Close examination will show that the shadows are not always theoretically correct – indeed, as time went by the 'rigorous determination' of shadows was replaced by approximations which became conventionalised. This was so in engineering; in architecture the proper determination of shadows was and is still taught. Today it is called

'Sciagraphy' and it is interesting to note that whilst these shadows are used as an aid in interpretation of drawings, the principles used hark back to the practical matter of determining shadows in sun-dialling.

Irrespective of their practical use in engineering, and possibly because of their retention in architecture, technical drawing courses in Britain at the end of the 19th century nearly all introduced the rigorous determination of shadows in the drawing theory part. An example is given in Fig. 57 taken from a book of *c*. 1880.* The problem is to determine the shadow of the cone on the cylinder surface. The method given is shown by the heavy broken lines with arrow heads; starting from the circular view of the cylinder one may trace light rays up to two points on the cone, one on the near side and one on the far side. These points are then 'revolved' into the plane of the paper and projected down onto a diameter of the cone's plan; thence revolved onto the shadow's edges on the cone, and finally projected from there to the plan of the cylinder, to meet the vertical projector from the point at which we started. In this particular case, there is a very much easier way of finding this shadow. This is shown by the fine dotted lines, which are not part of the original illustration. If the cylinder were not there, the light rays would continue to meet the horizontal plane. This point, for the rays chosen, can be projected down to the plan of where the shadow would be and thence onto the cylinder surface.

Many teachers at the time were not concerned with the direct usefulness or otherwise of such constructions; they contended that they were good geometrical exercises which helped the student to master thinking in three dimensions whilst drawing in two.

This, incidentally, is one of those areas in which one drawing system seems to have borrowed from the other. Whilst drawings of this type were presented as an extension of the British system of orthographic projection, they appear to have taken a lot from French books which were, of course, based on Mongean geometry.

Looking back, and going by the various books published at the time, there seems to have been some muddle as to what was the nature of engineering drawing. Binns, for example, reacted against courses which merely taught persons how to copy other drawings and he brought in his 'ABC of drawing' which was more or less a treatise on the axioms of orthographic projection. This became the theoretical basis of drawing instruction and it was added to in many

* *Practical Plane Geometry & Projection*, by Henry Angel.

directions – the work on shadows being an example. This, however, still all led to 'pure' drawing rather than to 'applied' drawing.

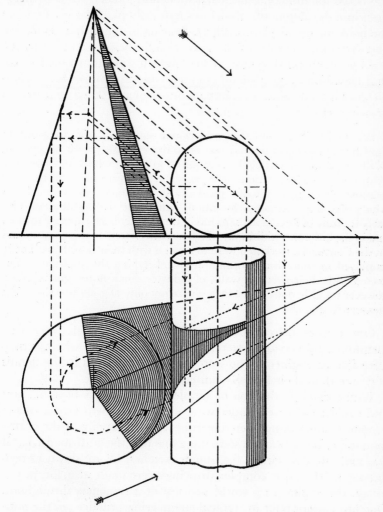

Fig. 57. Typical exercises in projecting shadows as introduced into British technical drawing courses in late 19th century. From *Practical Plane Geometry and Projections*, by Henry Angel, *c.* 1880.

Davidson made a start in changing direction in the series of books he wrote about 1870. The first books were on plane geometry and then projection. These were followed up by a series for various types of craftsmen and to a large extent used the knowledge provided in the earlier books. For instance, projection was applied in the books for stone masons, carpenters and joiners, while penetrations and developments of surfaces naturally played a vital part in the book for metal-plate workers. Bearing in mind that projection and systematic constructions were rapidly being accepted as the basis of technical drawing, at first sight it appears strange to see that Davidson's text-book for engineers and machinists had a completely different bias, a large part of it being devoted to freehand drawing. He wrote, for example:

It is highly important that a workman should be able to sketch at sight from any object he may see, or to draw roughly with his piece of chalk or pencil any article he is required to make; whilst, in these days of international exhibitions, the power of bringing away from other countries drawings of tools, mechanical appliances, or other things which may have attracted attention, cannot be over-estimated. The early training of foreign artisans has in this respect been superior to ours, and in the different exhibitions which have been held in this country and on the Continent, workmen were to be seen with their note-books busily employed in collecting information and sketching the appliances connected with their peculiar walks of industry. Such notes and sketches, however roughly done, must be a source not only of great usefulness but pleasure to them.[22]

One cannot help wondering whether the 'foreign workmen' mentioned by Davidson were, in fact, workmen, or whether they were foreign engineers who were far more interested in the details of design than their British counterparts.

Whilst mass production of simple items—such as buttons, pins and needles—was well under way (even the ancient Greeks mass-produced some things), engineering was still largely in the craftsman stage. If one wanted something one told the craftsman what it was and, after making a few rough sketches, he got down to producing it. Of course, complex drawings were made also, for, just as today, the engineering world was not of a sameness throughout. One just cannot refer to 'typical engineering practice' in the mid-19th century because it varied so much in different industries. Nevertheless, some idea of the state of the art can be gathered from this extract from Davidson's book.

Cog-Wheel. This is part of a Cog-Wheel—a name generally understood to mean a wheel in which the teeth are made of wood and mortised separately into an iron rim, in contra-distinction to *spur* wheels, in which the teeth are of iron and form part of the rim itself. These wheels were in general use in large machinery before the introduction of cast-iron wheels and are still very common in mills. The cogs are kept in their places by pins placed inside the rims, or by keys placed between their ends. In regard to such wheels, Prof. Willis says (Mechanics, art. 55):

The above construction of a toothed wheel has been partly imitated in modern mill-work, for it is found that if in a pair of wheels the teeth of one be of cast-iron and in the other of wood, that the pair work together with much less vibration and consequent noise, and that the teeth wear each other less than if both of the pair had had iron teeth.

Hence, in the best modern engines one wheel of every large-sized pair has wooden cogs fitted in it in the manner just described only, instead of employing a wooden wheel to receive them, a cast-iron wheel with mortises in the rim is employed.

In the present example the radius of the pitch is 1′ 3″; there are six arms and 48 teeth. The study should be worked to the scale of 3″ to the foot.[22] (Fig. 58.)

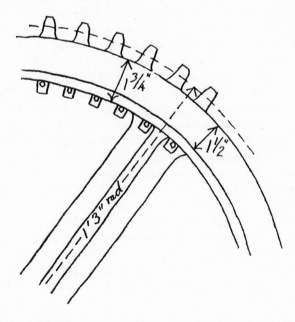

Fig. 58. Sketch as basis for drawing exercise, as much a test of technical knowledge as of pure drawing ability.

As Davidson had mentioned in the Preface to this book, the old method of teaching engineering drawing–copying drawings–had 'happily exploded' and there was a simple reason why it had so to explode. In architecture–from which engineering drawing then borrowed much–'art' played a very important part and the majority of drawing work was devoted to decoration, embellishment and such like. This sort of thing did not fit in well with engineering and it soon became apparent to some that one could not make any engineering drawing unless one knew what one was drawing, the function of the parts and the technology of manufacture.

This was significant for it introduced a trend which has continued to this day. Whereas Davidson's other drawing books dealt with projections, sections, developments, determining angles and so on – that is, pure drawing based on geometry–his book for engineers and machinists was more or less a review of various machine parts, their functions and materials. The major item in his book was the steam engine and most of the drawings were of cylinders, pistons, cottered connecting rods, eccentrics, etc., although some drawings were of parts of a 15-inch Whitworth lathe. Most older engineering readers will probably remember that such items appeared in the text-books they studied–which shows how little the teaching of engineering and drawing changed in, say, seventy years.

Towards the end of the 19th century British text-books began to condense into three more or less recognisable groups; books on pure drawing; books on machine drawing, which assumed a fundamental knowledge of orthographic projection, etc.; and books on machine design. The books on machine drawing really amounted to drawing exercises using as material various simple machine parts, in order that the draughtsman should instinctively develop a sense of the right shapes and proportions. The books on machine design contained drawings similar to the above, but they were based on mechanics and were more concerned with forces and stresses. Some authors tended to combine two of these three groups into one work; for example, *An Introduction to Machine Drawing and Design*, by D. A. Low, published in 1914.

The following note from this book is of interest to show how the accent had shifted from drawing as such to a knowledge of engineering parts.

In addition to the exercises given in this work, the student should practice making freehand sketches of machine details from actual machines or good models of them. Upon these sketches he should put the proper dimensions, got by direct measurement from the machine or model by himself. These sketches should be made in a note-book kept for the purpose, and no opportunity should be lost of inserting a sketch of any design which may be new to the student, always putting in the dimensions if possible. These sketches form excellent examples from which to make working drawings. The student should note any rules which he may meet with for proportioning machines, taking care, however, in each case to state the source of such information for his future guidance and reference.

As machine drawing is simply the application of the principles of descriptive geometry to the representation of machines, the student of the former subject, if he is not already acquainted with the latter, should commence to study it at once.[46]

Notice that the term 'descriptive geometry' is used in the last sentence. Following continental practice this term came into regular use in both Britain and America to cover 'pure' drawing theory and practice, but this does not mean that Mongean geometry suddenly came into use as such – it was and is a convenient name for a group of principles and constructions which have varying ancestries but which, because of their very nature, have much in common with what Monge collected under this title.

Fig. 59 is typical of the drawings or sketches students would be expected to make in the early years of this century. A sketch-book full of such drawings took the place of the many makers' catalogues draughtsmen use today, for at this time one more or less designed and made a machine completely – there were no specialist firms from whom ball or journal bearings, etc. could be ordered, let alone bought off the shelf.

Whilst the axioms of orthographic projection continued in Britain, a variation appeared about 1880. Where this modification came from is somewhat obscure, although the general background is clear and of some interest.

19th-century Britain was a continuation of the Industrial Revolution. Training in 'the manufactures' was through apprenticeship and the very success of this scheme in the past delayed proper and widespread technical education by some generations.

Some attempts had been made to introduce scientific instruction by Lord Brougham and other educationalists who formed the Society for the Diffusion of Useful Knowledge. The book on *Practical Geometry* by Thomas Bradley quoted a number of times in this work was published by that Society. However, there was great confusion over the nature of technical education. Some saw it as attempts to train craftsmen in schools instead of in industry and thereby strongly opposed it.

We have already noted that much formal education given to

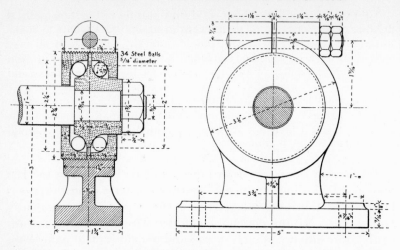

Fig. 59. A text-book sketch of a ball-bearing *c.* 1900. Students and draughtsmen were expected to compile sketch-books of such items for reference before engineering parts could be bought 'off the shelf'.

engineering students in the first half of the 19th century was based upon architectural practice. Indeed, the records show a vast confusion over the years between applied scientific knowledge, design, art and drawing. When representations were made to parliament that the design of British industry was falling short of that of its competitors, the Government set up a Select Committee, with the result that a number of Royal Academicians and others interested in art attempted to establish schools of design. They did not succeed in their purpose and, to cut a long and dismal story short, after much pressure by competent authorities, in August 1881, a Royal Commission was appointed 'to inquire into the instruction of the industrial classes of certain foreign countries in technical and other subjects, for the purpose of comparison with that of the corresponding classes in this country; and into the influence of such instruction on manufacturing and other industries at home and abroad'.

This Royal Commission made a good job of its work. A first Report was issued in 1882 and a second Report in 1884. Naturally, the Commission could not help but be struck by the evident importance attached to drawing—technical and otherwise—by European educationalists, particularly in France and Belgium, and also by the very thorough, systematic and enthusiastic way in which drawing instruction was carried on from the primary schools right up through to the advanced schools and colleges.

Professor W. Ripper, of the Technical School, Sheffield, writing in 1892 of the Commission's findings in this respect said:

All this was in painful contrast to the drawing instruction given in this country [Britain]. In 1886 drawing was taught to not more than one eighth of the scholars in our elementary schools, and the standard of requirement was by no means creditable for a manufacturing nation. Considerable improvement has happily been made since that date. By the Code of 1890 drawing is now compulsory in boys' schools, and the drawing requirements are modified and rendered much more thorough and servicable as a course of instruction.

Whilst no figures seem to be available directly referring to technical drawing the following will give some idea of the change in a period of thirty years. In 1862 there were 70 schools engaged in science and technical teaching in Britain with 2,543 pupils; in 1891 there were 2,164 such schools with 148,408 pupils. This shows a remarkable improvement; one can, however, look at this the other way round to see how backward Britain was in the field of technical education as late as 1862.

The compulsory introduction of drawing into schools' curricula meant compiling syllabuses, setting examinations and so on, and jointly with this effort we find a new crop of drawing text-books being produced. It is amongst these books that the new orthographic projection variation arose, although how it came into being is obscure.

In Mongean descriptive geometry only two planes of projection were postulated. Other theoretical planes were introduced as might be necessary to solve problems, these being represented on the planes of projection by their traces. In British orthographic projection up to this time, as depicted earlier by examples from the works of Davidson and Binns, two and sometimes three planes of projection were used, these being at right angles to one another. The new concept introduced planes in arbitrary positions as auxiliary planes of projection. This idea is illustrated in principle in Fig. 60. In (a) the point P in space is defined or recorded by its two projections p_1 and p_2 on the vertical and horizontal reference planes. Now suppose an inclined plane III is introduced, perpendicular to the vertical plane VVV, but at an angle to the horizontal plane HHH. The projection of point P onto this new plane is p_3. Suppose we now consider not just a point but the line Pp_1; its projection onto III is the same as its projection onto the horizontal plane HHH. In (b) the horizontal plane is dispensed with. We have the original vertical plane of projection, *VVV*, and a new auxiliary plane of projection, *III*. Another plane *OOO* is then introduced, this being perpendicular

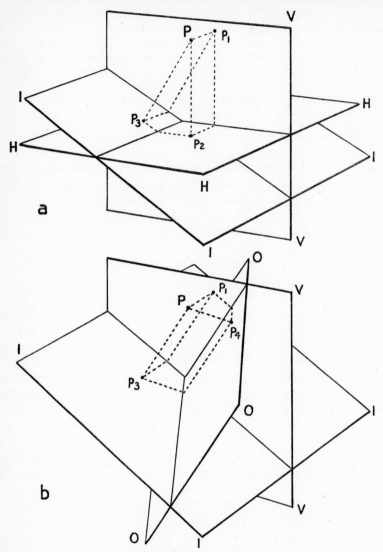

Fig. 60. The theoretical basis for projection on to auxiliary planes as appeared in a new generation of text-books introduced in Britain in late 19th century.

to plane *III*, but oblique to the vertical plane. As before, the projections of P are p_1, p_3 and p_4, the latter being on this second auxiliary plane of projection. Again, as before, one dimension, Pp_3, is the same whether projected onto plane VVV, or onto plane OOO.

This theoretical idea is shown applied to the projection of a solid shape in Fig. 61 – in this case the same hexagonal prism used by Binns in Fig. 55. For clarity the projected views are opened out rather more than was the contemporary practice. The original

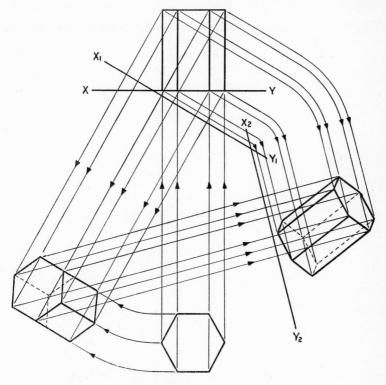

Fig. 61. Projection on to auxiliary planes as practised. For clarity the views are spaced further apart than was contemporary practice.

plan and front view are at the centre, the intersection of the horizontal and vertical planes of projection being the line XY. A new line X_1Y_1 is then drawn, this representing the intersection of the inclined auxiliary plane and the vertical plane. The new plan is projected from the original front view, by projectors perpendicular to X_1Y_1, and from the original plan. The widths in the two plan views do not change, being similar to the projections of Pp_1 in Fig. 60. In a similar way another line X_2Y_2 may be drawn and a new view of the hexagonal prism produced on the second auxiliary plane.

To those of us familiar with orthographic projection, Figs. 61 and 55 may be considered to be the same. If, in Fig. 55, we take out the two centre views and superimpose them on the views to the left so that the two front views coincide we have, in effect, the left half of Fig. 61. We can do the same with the right and centre pairs of views in Fig. 55 so that the two like plans are superimposed when we get the right half of Fig. 61. It seems likely that this is how this new arrangement of views came about; that is, it was a convenient way of overcoming the necessity of drawing some outlines twice in order to get auxiliary projections. The projection onto new planes as displayed in Fig. 60 would then be a rationalisation of this layout so that the whole could be presented for teaching purposes in a tidy, formal way.

Although, on a certain level, we can see that these two methods amount to the same thing, educationally they do rely upon different ideas; in one the object is moved; in the other new planes of projection are supposed.

In time this new kind of exercise in solid geometry, which required the student to become facile at true multiple plane drawing, tended to be dropped by educationalists. The encroachment of so many other subjects into the syllabuses of engineering courses continually whittled down the time that could be devoted to drawing, with the result that the theoretical basis of engineering drawing was passed across to students simply by showing that any solid body could be defined by making three projections of it on three mutually perpendicular planes.

This is really an erroneous view, as many a student finds out in later life. Three views of some object are adequate so long as the object is of such a shape that all its faces are parallel to one or other of the three planes of projection. If the shape of the body is such that many, if not all, of its faces (or axes, etc.) are not parallel to the three principal planes, the drawing becomes less adequate. It defines the body, true, but inadequately for those who want to use the drawing. An analogy to this is the case of depicting a cone by its circular plan and its triangular side elevation. In a sense this defines the surface, since from this given information only one surface can exist; but the shape of this surface, as a development, has to be deduced from the given views in the form of another drawing before one can actually make the cone from sheet metal.

Coming back to rectilineal shapes, consider Fig. 62. The shape of this object is defined in the three views marked A, B and C, since the distances between any two corner points can be determined in terms of vertical and horizontal lengths in the x, y and z directions of co-ordinate geometry. The form is 'pinned down' because only one shape of object will give these three projections. These three views can, however, also be considered as inadequate by themselves since, except for the base upon which the object stands, the true shapes of the various parts are not shown. What is, for instance, the true angle between the two parts? This can be shown by view

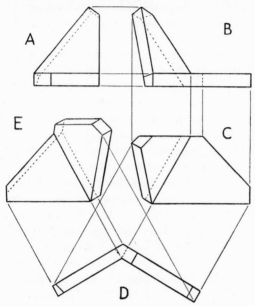

Fig. 62. Demonstrating the necessity for using auxiliary planes of projection when portraying objects whose planes and edges are not at right angles.

D, a projection onto an auxiliary plane. From this we can also produce another view, E, on another auxiliary plane to show the true shape of the oblique faces in the first three views. What is perhaps more interesting from the student's point of view, is that views D and E are necessary in order to be able to draw views A, B and C. Indeed, views A and B are really redundant; the lower three views are quite adequate to describe the part and, although these are three in number, they are not projections onto mutually perpendicular planes. The planes of projection are selected arbitrarily to exhibit true shape information.

In education, this problem is still not really solved. How many views are necessary to describe adequately some given three-dimensional rectilineal object? Working from purely theoretical directions, it can be shown that an object with X faces needs X views, although this number is reduced by symmetry and parallelism between faces. Some teachers have tried to introduce this rule, together with others covering internal features, etc., but in practice these are difficult to apply. Another idea is based upon the similarity between the operations of drawing and those of actually forming parts; this leads to the rule that whatever views are necessary to draw the object are also necessary for those who are to make it.

In some ways the above is a digression, but it does help to show that even to this day the fundamentals of drawing have still not been finally solidified into doctrines beyond dispute.

Apart from this practically oriented drawing, by 1900 the value of drawing as 'a powerful engine of calculation' was recognised in higher educational circles in Britain and descriptive geometry, very much on Mongean lines, was introduced into college syllabuses for science students. At this time the treatment was 'pure' but it affected later text-books and teaching at other levels.

One of the interesting books to appear at this time was Harrison's and Baxandall's *Practical Plane and Solid Geometry*. In particular we may note that these authors still condemned the adherence to Euclid, though for different reasons from those expressed by Cunningham. Euclid's system of pure geometry, they pointed out, led only to the use of a straight edge, a pencil, compasses, and a single plane surface on which to draw. The increasing use of the T-square and triangular set-square had caused Euclid's restrictions to be relaxed a little, but were we not still in leading-strings? As well as using, in theory at least, as many planes as we wanted to draw upon, why should not any amount of devices, mechanical and otherwise, be used to facilitate drawing?

There is something very modern about these sentiments.

14

The American Scene : First and Third
Angle Projections

DURING the Second World War, when a great many technical drawings flowed backwards and forwards across the Atlantic, one of the most annoying differences of conventions was that used for the arrangement of views. Whilst what is known as 'first angle' projection was the accepted standard in Britain, and was used almost throughout Europe and the greater part of the Commonwealth, both the U.S.A. and Canada were using 'third quadrant' (or angle) projection. Today, considerable efforts are being made to eliminate this difference, at least in Britain, where industry has long been encouraged to change to American projection. A complete change-over seems unlikely, however, because of the association of many British companies with continental ones.

Where production drawings are concerned, 'first' and 'third' angle projections are merely conventions–like inches or centimetres, one can work equally well in either system. Initially, however, these methods of projection were based on what appeared at the time to be important conceptual differences.

Whilst in very early technical drawings the simple idea of plans and elevations arose almost naturally, their arrangement on paper, one to another, was merely a matter of convenience. The Gatling Gun drawing shown in Fig. 63 is reminiscent of this type of layout; it is not truly an example, as Patent drawings have their own peculiar reasons for existence, though they have retained some fundamental features of more orthodox engineering drawings. With improvements in drawing instruments and equipment, convenience in layout meant not so much filling the paper to advantage, as ease of execution. Accordingly views of an object–a building or machine–tended to be drawn lined up with one another in some way. In some cases it was only the front and side views which became aligned indirectly because they were drawn upon one straight line representing the ground. This brought out an advantage in that heights in the front view could be transferred to the side view

155

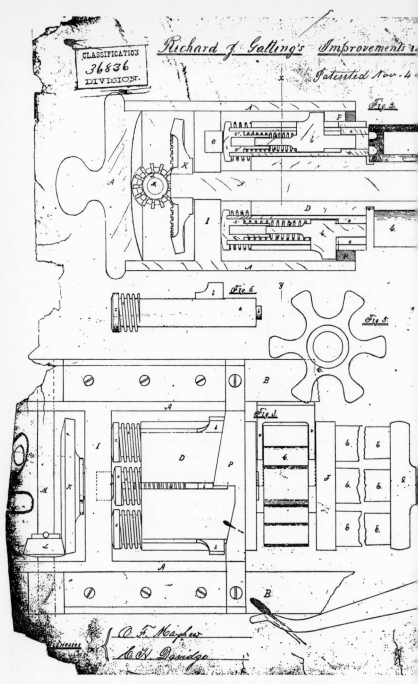

Richard J. Gatling's Improvements

Patented Nov. 4

Fig. 2

Fig. 6

Fig. 5

Fig. 3

O. F. Mayhew

C. K. Davidge

Fig. 63. Reproduction of the original Patent Drawing, dated November 4, 1862, of Richard J. Gatling's Revolving Battery Gun, in the files of the U.S. Patent Office. Reproduced from an enlargement on Kodagraph Projection Film Estar

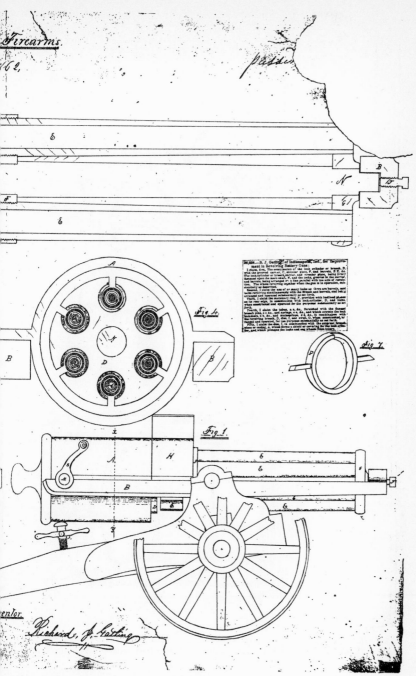

Base, which was made from a microfilm negative of the original, and made available by the Eastman Kodak Company, Rochester, N. Y., U. S. A.

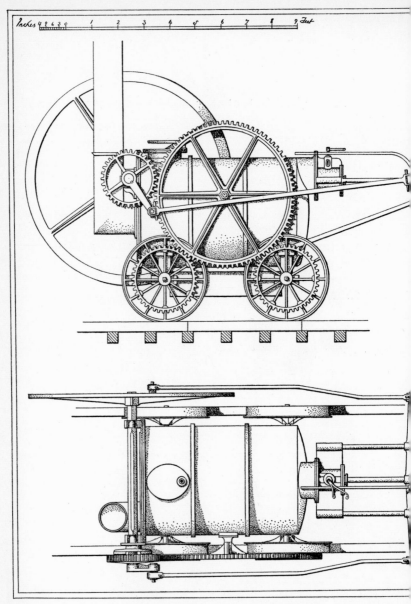

Fig. 64. Copy of a drawing of Trevithick's Newcastle Locomotive 1804. The original, in the Science Museum, London, is finished with water-colour washes

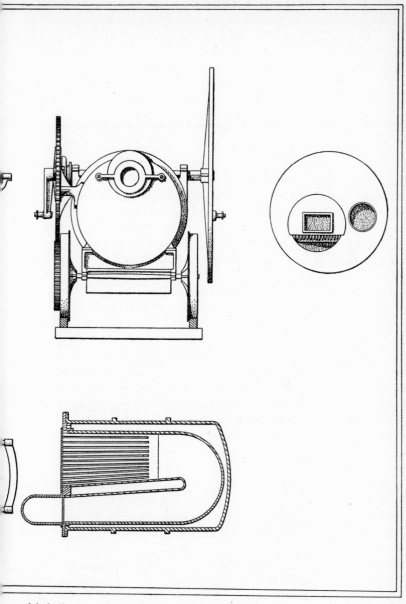

and is believed to have been the work of Richard Trevithick himself. See also Fig. 69.

simply by drawing a line parallel to the ground line, instead of transferring them by dividers. Eventually the plan came to be positioned directly in line with the front view so that lengths could be transferred through vertical lines, instead of by dividers–just as Dürer had demonstrated in the 16th century.

A typical engineering drawing showing various views arranged in this way is that of the Newcastle Locomotive in Fig. 64. This is believed to be the actual work of Trevithick and the original is now displayed in the Science Museum, London. Whilst the various views are aligned for ease of execution, the relationships between the views are not consistent. For instance, the plan, which is a view from on *top*, is drawn *below* the front elevation; to be consistent, therefore, one would expect a view from the *right* of this front elevation to be drawn on the *left*, whereas in fact it is placed on the right. The extreme right view, a part view of the engine looking from the left of the front elevation, has no logical position at all, except that it is the same height above the ground as the other views of the boiler.

Everything in this drawing suggests that the arrangement is simply for convenience of execution. (The Canadian drawing shown in Fig. 74 should also be seen.) It is none the worse for this 'loose' arrangement and we can easily assemble the views in our mind to get a mental picture of the real engine. However, the reasons for this are that the object depicted is fairly simple, and that we are already familiar with the nature of a vehicle. Now for a change, look at Fig. 65, which is based upon an engraving of about 1830–it illustrates something made earlier and it may be based upon an original design drawing of about 1770. In comparison, this is a drawing of an unfamiliar object–indeed there is nothing to tell us even which is the top. This is not at all easy to interpret. Try to imagine the machine in the solid. Some of the difficulties arise from the fact that it is not a very good drawing in detail, but the main obstruction lies in the peculiar arrangement of the various views, and particularly in the inconsistency of the relationship between any two views.

There was, and is, therefore, a very good case for making engineering drawings consistent in arrangement so as to make the interpretation, as well as the execution, as easy as possible. Referring to Trevithick's Locomotive drawing, either the plan could be placed *above* the front view to make the relationship between these views the same as that existing between the side and front views, or the side view could be taken from the right and placed at the *left* of the front view. There is really little to choose between which course is adopted, though there have been protagonists emphasising the advantages of one system over the other for a long time.

In Europe there was really no decision to make. All drawing on the Continent was based on Monge's descriptive geometry, and his method of projection onto planes produced that type of arrangement in which the plan of an object was drawn beneath the object's front elevation – and similarly, the left side of an object was drawn

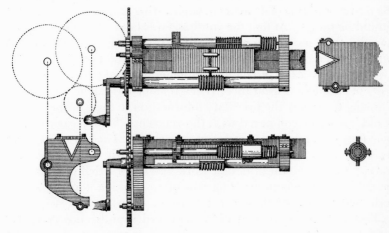

Fig. 65. An engraving showing the special screw-cutting machine used by Jesse Ramsden in 1775 to cut the worm and worm-wheel hob for his dividing engine.

at the right of the front view and vice versa. Although British drawing practice had grown up independently, its orthographic projection system of axioms likewise had its basis in the projection of views on to planes and this led to the same type of arrangement.

In America the situation was different. Industrially the u.s.a. lagged Europe in the first half of the 19th century, but from 1850 onwards there was an expansion of such colossal proportions that it can only be compared with the Industrial Revolution in Britain. When the Chicago World Fair was held in 1893 visitors from abroad were most surprised at what they saw.

The American expansion was not, however, a simple repetition of what had happened in Britain earlier; the phasing was quite different. Although, as far as dates are concerned, the beginnings of technical education in America were roughly contemporary with those in Britain, on these countries' industrial time scales the u.s.a. started much earlier. There was, of course, considerable migration of various Europeans to the u.s.a.; on the one hand these people brought over some of the French and German ideas of education, on the other hand, the mixture of races led to there being no accepted tradition to replace, such as the deep-rooted apprenticeship system in Britain. It is true that there was some resistance to the early 'college-trained' draughtsmen, but this broke down as training improved.

To begin with there were the inevitable difficulties of isolating the nature and role of drawing in engineering, and in deciding what should be taught. At first the emphasis was heavily on teaching the handling and use of materials. College-trained draughtsmen could shrink paper onto the drawing-board, mix coloured inks, paint blemish-free washes of colour and generally make drawings from copy of excellent appearance. When it came to making an original drawing to convey the necessary information to the workmen, they could hardly be compared with the veterans who had earned their positions through long, hard-won experience. The demands upon drawing were, of course, not comparable with what we expect today; a fair amount of design work was still carried out through modelling, and manufacturing was often through copying a material pattern rather than working from a drawing.

Technical drawing education improved rapidly, however, not least because many worthy men from industry were far-sighted enough to go into teaching. These educationalists did a good job because they perceived the true functions of engineering drawings and many books were written on the art of shape description through drawings. The various teachers or 'professors' did not, however, always agree amongst themselves upon what should be taught or how it should be taught, and it is unlikely that there will ever be unanimity in this subject. The aspect which probably created most heated argument was the method to be used in arranging views. Frederic G. Higbee[39] has described this war as 'amusing' but it was, nevertheless, of some consequence.

Broadly speaking there were two bases to this argument; one was the practical one of which layout was the most simple to draw or read; the other, somewhat tied up with the former, was how the arrangement was arrived at in theory, and was mainly the concern of the academics.

The alternative approaches were given very clearly in a book by

Joshua Rose, published in Philadelphia in 1883. Fig. 66 demonstrates the alternative systems and the text accompanying this was as follows:

There are two systems of placing the different views of a piece. In the first the views are presented as the piece would present itself if it were

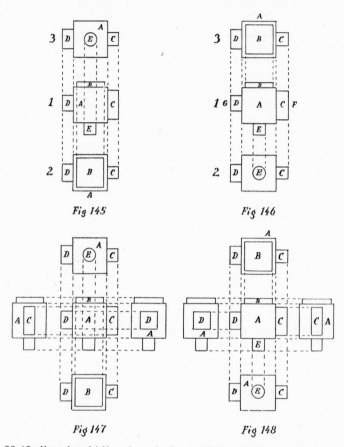

Fig 145

Fig 146

Fig 147

Fig 148

Fig. 66. 'Indirect' and 'direct' revolution applied to projection or the arrangement of views in multi-view drawing, as illustrated by Joshua Rose, 1883, in U.S.A.

laid upon the paper for the side view, and then turned or rolled upon the paper for the other views, as shown in fig. 145, in which the piece consists of five sections or members, marked respectively A, B, C, D and E. Now if the piece were turned or rolled so that the end face of B were uppermost, and the member E was beneath, it will, by the operation of turning it, have assumed the position in the lower view marked 2; while if it were turned over upon the paper in the opposite direction it would assume the position marked 3. This gives to the mind a clear idea of the various views and positions; but it possesses some disadvantages; thus, if position 1 is a side elevation or view of the piece, as it stands when in place on the machine, then E is naturally the bottom member; but it is shown in the top view of the drawing, hence what is actually the bottom view of the piece (position 3) becomes the top view of the drawing. A second disadvantage is that if we desire to put in dotted lines to show how one view is derived from the other, and denote corresponding parts, then these dotted lines must be drawn across the face of the drawing, making it less distinct; thus the dotted lines connecting stem E in position 1 to E in position 3 pass across the faces of both A and B of position 1.

In a large drawing, or one composed of many members or parts, it would, therefore, be out of the question to mark in the dotted lines. A further disadvantage in a large drawing is that it is necessary to go from one side of the drawing to the other to see the construction of the same part.

To obviate these difficulties, a modern method is to suppose the piece, instead of rolling on the paper, to be lifted from it, turned around to present the required view, and then moved upward on the paper for a top view, sideways for a side view, and below for a bottom view. Thus the three views of the piece in fig. 145 would be as in fig. 146, where position 2 is obtained by supposing the piece to be lifted from position 1, the bottom face turned uppermost, and the piece moved down the paper to position 2, which is a bottom view of the piece, and the bottom view of the drawing. Similarly, if the piece be lifted from position 1, and the top face in that figure is turned uppermost, and the piece is then slid upwards on the paper, view 3 is obtained, being a top view of the piece as it lies in position 1, and the top view in the drawing. Now suppose we required to find the shape of member B, then in fig. 145 we require to look at the top of position 1, and then down below to position 2. But in fig. 146 we have the side view and end view both together, while the dotted lines do not require to cross the face of the side view.

Now suppose we take a similar piece, and suppose its end faces as F, G, to have holes in them which require to be shown in both views, and under the one system of drawing would, if the dotted lines were drawn across, appear as in fig. 147, whereas under the other system the drawing would appear as in fig. 148. And it follows that if it is necessary to draw dotted lines from one view to the other, it is best to adopt the new system.[62]

Although Rose referred to the 'new system', from other writings it seems that what was wanted was simply a clear recognisable system in place of no system at all, rather than a displacing of an existing order of things. Whilst the above quotation pleads the case for what ultimately became known as third angle projection on the count of being able to project the easier from one view to another, it also demonstrated the 'moving object' principle of positioning the views.

Other writers preferred the 'moving paper' principle,* as for instance:

> . . . the horizontal and vertical projections are made with the object at rest on the horizontal plane. To illustrate, a brick will do. First, plan, brick lying down flat, view from top shows it eight inches long, four inches wide. Second, side elevation, board shoved behind brick, and figure of brick marked upon it, two inches high, eight inches long. Third, end elevation, board raised on the right and figure of brick drawn on it, two inches high, four wide. . . .

Commenting, with his tongue in his cheek, on the many ideas on these lines put forward, Oberlin Smith wrote in 1875:

> The writers of the recent essays upon the above seem to dwell particularly upon the doctrines of descriptive geometry, although some of them ring the changes upon other imaginative methods of conceiving what a drawing means, such as walking around the object represented, or climbing up on top of it, or burrowing underneath it, or looking at it through transparent paper, or through glass, or having its various sides depicted upon paper which may be supposed to be wrapped around it, and which afterwards may be peeled off, after the manner of skinning an orange, etc.
>
> This question of which way to project cannot in the nature of things be of such very great importance in itself, like theology, or so many good people would not differ regarding it. Let us then all strive to come to a common practice in the matter and meet upon common ground of *direct* revolution if we can, or *indirect* if we must. Let us remember, however, that America is all the time becoming less provincial and that this common ground should be international, rather than merely occidental.

It is of interest to note that he refers to the two systems of projection as those of 'direct' or 'indirect' revolution, and also that he gives his preference which, if referred to Rose's quotation, presumably meant first angle, especially as his plea for internationalism would have meant accepting this method. Indeed, it is difficult to find out when or how the modern terms 'first' and 'third' quadrant or angle came into use. In the first editions of the *Encyclopedia Brittanica* to devote space to descriptive geometry, Fig. 67 appears. The

---

* The two principles were often referred to as 'Position of Object' and 'Position of Observer'.

bold lines in the left drawing represent the edge views of two intersecting planes, analogous to the axes of plane Cartesian geometry. The four quadrants were labelled first, second, third and fourth, and in each quadrant a point was marked, A, B, C and D. The projections of these onto the reference planes gave A_1A_2, B_1B_2, etc. If then the vertical plane was swung over to coincide with the horizontal plane, these points' projections appeared as in the right drawing. All these projections were different and they were referred to as first, second, third and fourth quadrant respectively. The word 'angle' instead of 'quadrant' was often used later in Britain and is the term in use today. In practice, for the representation of solid objects, second and fourth angle projection were of no use, as the

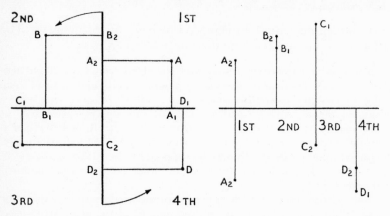

Fig. 67. First, second, third and fourth quadrant projections as illustrated in treatises on pure descriptive geometry, c. 1890.

two views would lie superimposed upon one another. First angle corresponds to the Mongean system of projection and that of British orthographic projection. Third angle corresponds with the arrangement eventually adopted in America.

Since from quite early times the American draughtsman was college trained, educationalists in general, and particularly text-book writers, played a very big part in the development of engineering drawing methods and conventions. They and most practising draughtsmen found third quadrant an easier system of arrangement than first angle and this so became the general practice, very little, if any, thought being given to Oberlin's suggestion that a universal practice should be aimed at.

The general adoption of third angle projection had some drawbacks, at least for a time. Although the term 'descriptive geometry' appears often in American writings of the last half of the 19th century, this should be interpreted in a very general way, and not as representing a complete system of axioms. At the time, engineering drawing in America meant more or less representing mechanical parts. Geometrical constructions in three dimensions had not to be cemented in with existing drawing practice. When at length Blessing and Darling wrote their book *The Elements of Descriptive Geometry* at the beginning of this century, they were obliged to deal with points, lines and planes in first angle projection, and solid geometry in third angle. This may have been a hardship for the students, changing over in the middle of the course, but they probably gained in the long run.

Blessing and Darling wrote their book originally as college course notes as they felt it was time descriptive geometry was introduced into university instruction; they were based upon Monge's work as developed later by French writers, and from reading the Preface to this book one could be forgiven if one assumed that Mongean geometry was new in America. This, of course, was not so. Monge's descriptive geometry arrived in the United States in the person of Claude Crozet, who joined the faculty of the U.S. Military Academy at West Point in 1816. Colonel Crozet, known today as the Father of Descriptive Geometry in the U.S.A., was a graduate of the École Polytechnique, and had been an artillery officer under Napoleon. He was engaged to teach engineering to the cadets at West Point but found that he would have to teach them mathematics first. Crozet's *A Treatise on Descriptive Geometry* was written for use at the Military Academy and was published in 1821. This was probably the first book in English on this subject.

Another more extensive text on descriptive geometry was published in 1826 by Professor Charles Davies, also of West Point, probably after Crozet had left the Academy to become Chief Engineer of the State of Virginia. In America, as in Britain, descriptive geometry was taken up very early by the military, though its Mongean form became diluted over the years with indigenous drawing practices.

The First World War accelerated the industrial growth of the U.S.A. and, among much else, considerable attention was turned towards the place of the drawing office in the scheme of things and, in particular, the kind of knowledge the draughtsman should have. Between then and now men like Anthony, the Reid

Brothers, Jamison, Svensen and French have produced text-books which explored the field of technical drawing as never before. Seeing it as a 'graphic language' there was a progressive dropping of the term 'mechanical drawing'. Professor French tried to introduce the general expression 'engineering drawing'; Professor Anthony suggested the wider use of the word 'graphics', while Carl Lars Svensen called his book *Essentials of Drafting*.

This trend continues to this very day. In the second edition of Hoelscher and Springer's *Engineering Drawing and Geometry* (1962) one sees many of the first edition chapters dropped and more general ones substituted. Chapters on 'special kinds' of drawing – machine drawing, tool drawing, etc. – have disappeared, since engineering shapes are continually changing and the philosophy now in such books is to provide a comprehensive set of graphical techniques which can be used widely by engineers within a rapidly changing technology.

When, by the time of the First World War at the latest, third angle projection had been adopted as general practice in America, and when more and more constructional drawing of a descriptive geo-metry nature was introduced into education, it became increasingly necessary to combine the two. This was done by invoking a physical model comparable to Monge's two planes of projection, so that third angle projection could be explained in terms of projection on to planes. This model was the 'glass box' shown in Fig. 68. The object being drawn was imagined to be inside a glass box with the outlines projected orthographically onto the top, bottom and sides. These views as seen from the outside were, when the box was 'opened out' or developed, then arranged in third angle. Generally, the 'glass box' was only a mental conception to aid in explanation, but a material glass (more often perspex) box has in many instances been used in colleges for tuition purposes with a real object inside.[50]

It is interesting to note that this model leads logically to the pro-duction of six related views, since the box has six faces, although only the required number may be chosen for any particular draw-ing. British orthographic projection in its pure state led to three views, while the original Mongean principle produced two views.

The interest in technical education in America is reflected in the formation of the Society for the Promotion of Engineering Educa-tion, founded at the World Fair in Chicago in 1893, and the interest in engineering drawing education in particular led to the forma-tion of the Engineering Drawing Division of the Society in 1928.

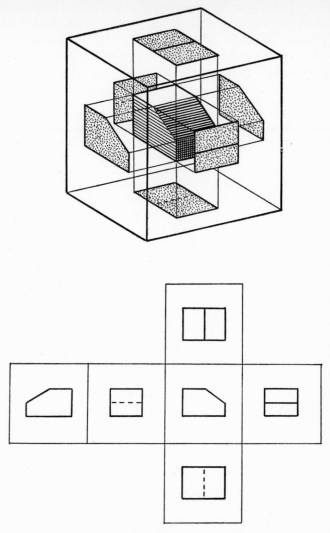

Fig. 68. *Top*: The 'Glass Box' used in America to demonstrate third quadrant projection.
  Bottom: The 'Glass Box' developed, or opened out, leads to six basic views.

The s.p.e.e. changed its name to the American Society for Engineering Education in 1947 and, since 1958, the Drawing Division has been known as the Engineering Graphics Division.

The First World War stretched the industrial capacity of all the participants and, since by this time the production drawing had become a key element in engineering, in the following years efforts were made to standardise drawing practice. The first American Drawing Standard was approved in 1935, and naturally, third angle projection was adopted without hesitation as it was, by then, general American practice.

15

Conventions and Standards in Drawings

In the field of engineering drawing proper, that is, the planning and depiction of the real complex shapes necessary in machinery, the simple methods of projection have never been enough. They have been supplemented progressively by so-called conventions. These have had and still have two reasons for existence; one is to ensure the clear interpretation of drawings by the viewer; the other has been to make the draughtsman's work less arduous and time consuming. There are so many conventions in modern engineering drawing that it would be hopeless to try to trace all their origins, and no doubt rather boring to read about them too. Some conventions have now disappeared, some have stayed, whilst others have been developed.

We have already seen one convention which came and went—that of using shadows on drawings. Where two projections were given one did not have to use the shadows to estimate dimensions perpendicular to the paper surface. Nevertheless the shadows were helpful in interpretation, because wherever one saw a shadow against a line one recognised which side of the line was material and which space. This led to a system of 'shadow-lining' in which edges vertical to the plane of the paper and in shade were made darker, that is they were drawn heavier or thicker, than those edges in the light. An example is shown in Fig. 69. This convention probably also originated in architectural drawing and it was used almost instinctively by Trevithick, Watt and other draughtsmen in the engineering world at the end of the 18th century. It is still used as normal practice for illustrations in some of our leading technical journals. It began to disappear when drawings were reproduced by the blue-print process, for these were virtually negatives, and those edges in shadow consequently appeared lighter instead of darker.

The introduction of simple drawing reproduction processes had quite a large effect on conventions, in particular the usefulness of colour on drawings disappeared, as the colours did not reproduce. Since most modern draughtsmen never come into contact with colour, it might be of some interest to quote from a leading text-book of 1914.

A first class working drawing should be prepared in the following manner. It must first be carefully outlined in pencil and then inked in. After this all parts cut by planes of section should be coloured, the colours used indicating the materials of which the parts are made. Parts which are

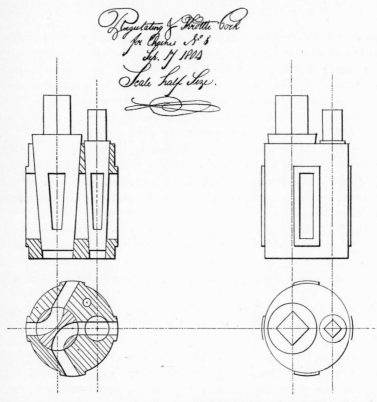

Fig. 69. Another drawing prepared for Trevithick's Newcastle Locomotive 1804 (see Fig. 64). Notice that the views on the right are the same as those on the left except that the latter are sectioned. The technique of shade-lining has been used, the thickening of lines giving the effect of edges in shadow. The original is in the Science Museum, London.

round may also be lightly shaded with the brush and colours to suit the materials. The centre lines are now inked in with red (or blue) ink. The red ink may be prepared by rubbing down the cake of crimson lake, and the blue ink in like manner from the cake of Prussian blue, but good coloured drawings inks may now be bought in bottles and, if they are waterproof inks, lines drawn with them may be put on the drawing before colouring it. Next come the distance or dimension lines, which should be put in with blue (or red) ink, depending upon which colour was used for the centre lines. Dimension and centre lines are best put in of different colour. The arrow-heads at the ends of the dimension lines are now put in with black ink, and so are the figures for the dimensions. The arrow-heads and the figures should be made with a common writing pen. The dimensions should be put on neatly.

The importance of putting the dimensions on a working drawing may here be pointed out. If the drawing is not dimensioned, the workman must get his sizes from the drawing by applying his rule or a suitable scale. Now this operation takes time and is very liable to error. Time is therefore saved and the chance of error reduced by marking the sizes in figures.

In practice it is not usual to send original drawings from the drawing office to the workshop, but copies only. The copies may be produced by various 'processes', or they may be tracings drawn by hand. Most commonly the copies are blue-prints made from tracings in ink. Few engineers ink in their original drawings, they leave them in pencil. . . .

First go over the part to be coloured with the brush and clean water for the purpose of damping it. Next dry with clean blotting paper to take off any superfluous water. Then take another brush with the colour and, beginning at the top, work from left to right and downwards. If it is necessary to recolour any part let the first coating dry before beginning. If the area to be coloured is small or in a narrow strip, the previous damping with water may be dispensed with.

Engineers have adopted certain colours to represent particular materials; these are given in the following table:

Material	Colour
Cast Iron	Payne's grey or neutral tint.
Wrought Iron	Purple.
Brass	Gamboge with a little sienna or a very little red added.
Copper	A mixture of crimson lake and gamboge, the former colour predominating.
Lead	Light Indian ink with a very little indigo added.
Brickwork	Crimson lake and burnt sienna.
Firebrick	Yellow and Vandyke brown.
Greystone	Light sepia or pale Indian ink with a little Prussian blue added.
Soft woods	For ground work, pale tint of sienna.
Hard woods	For ground work, pale tint of sienna with a little red added.
	For graining woods use darker tint with a greater proportion of red.[46]

In certain industries and for particular types of work, drawings are still coloured very much according to this table and the recommendations in the current British drawing standard are very similar.

Indeed, we must recognise that before the days of positive standardisation, text-books of this kind did a great service in tending to standardise drawing practices.

The increasing use of drawing reproduction methods which only reproduced lines was a major contribution towards the dropping of colours on drawings. Where shape was concerned a larger number of line drawings was more reliable than a few drawings relying on shadows, and where materials were concerned the answer was, of course, simply to use words to describe the material of a part. Some persons would not, however, accept this and some very queer practices were put forward in various books, though none seem to have been adopted.

One of these was an attempt to translate colour into terms of lines. Full line shading—a series of parallel lines then called hatching—sloping to the left, say, would represent red, while similar lines sloping to the right would be yellow. The two superimposed would then represent orange, the mixture of red and yellow—and a complicated code for all colours made up from the three primary colours was put forward. Although there was something dreadfully logical about this, it missed completely the nature of colour and our interpretation of it. In any event, it failed to recognise another reason for the dropping of colour from drawings—the increasing number of different metals and alloys being used in engineering.

The above suggestion was based on the practice of hatching, a technique whose origins stretch into the distant past. The idea probably arose through people drawing on clay tablets; when they marked in a lot of lines to represent hair, the dark shadows in the hollows of the lines made the whole area appear darker. The technique was taken up by some Middle Age artists. Polidore d' Caravaggio made a number of frescoes in Rome, where he used only a single colour, producing the shading by close parallel lines. In the art world the method became known as *graffito* or *peintures hachées*.

Hatching was used very seriously and cleverly in early printing. Pictures were first printed from woodcuts and later from fine engravings on metal plates. The technique demanded line work and fine hatching was the natural way to deal with shading. Since pictures and technical drawing merged almost completely at one time, it is difficult to say when hatching was taken over for sectioning as it is used today, but it was employed in this way by most of the early engineers proper, Murdoch, Watt, Nasmythe, and so on. As time went by, section lining became a convention and the lines were drawn further and further apart until there was no suggestion of imitating a tone or shade.

The broken line goes back so far that it is unrealistic to try to trace its origins. It was used, for example, to represent imaginary lines in some of the sun-dialling drawings shown earlier. Monge, and many earlier geometers, had need to differentiate between various lines and, besides full lines, we find lines made up from long dashes, short dashes and even rows of dots. Later dashes and dots were combined as 'chain' lines for even more differentiation. Printing may also have had a bearing on this development. Whereas upon a single drawing different lines could be made to stand out by using various colours, printing in one colour, usually black, demanded something different. Since illustrations were reproduced by the use of woodcuts, and later engravings, variations in line thicknesses was not very reliable and open to misinterpretation through under- or over-inking. Broken lines were ideally suited to this medium and were easily accomplished on woodcuts as a line, standing proud, could be given a succession of nicks.

In order to make engineering drawings clear it was necessary to use many of these variations, but they were employed quite arbitrarily until text-books of the late 19th century tended towards some measure of standardisation. Centre lines were often full lines or broken lines until the chain line was generally accepted. Eventually, of course, a standard appeared and the recommendations made for lines on engineering drawings in the earliest British drawing standard are shown in Fig. 70 bottom left. For comparison the recommendations from the current standard, issued twenty-six years later, are shown in Fig. 70 right. There are a few additions, but the recommendations are substantially the same.

Although text-books had done quite a lot to unify drawing practice, the war years of 1914–18 had shown up very clearly the difficulties inherent in non-standard drawing practices. As is usual in war-time, there was an all-out effort, and drawings originating in one quarter had often to be distributed amongst many firms in order to produce the goods quickly. The result was that shortly after the war a positive effort was made towards standardisation. The British Engineering Standards Association, which had grown out of a committee set up by the professional engineering institutions, was approached by the military authorities and in due course British Standard Drawing Office Practice appeared in 1927.

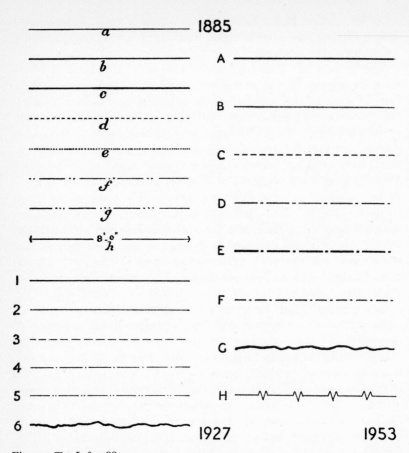

Fig. 70. *Top Left*: 1885.

Various lines used on engineering drawings in late 19th century, taken from *Practical Problems & Lines for Working Drawings*, Anon. London, 1885. No particular uses for the different lines were suggested.

Bottom Left: 1927.

Lines taken from B. S. 308: 1927.
(1) Outline (thick).
(2) Dimension line (thin). Projection line for dimension line. Sectioning.
(3) Hidden detail.
(4) Centre line. Path line (locus).
(5) Cutting plane or section line except where it follows a centre line, in which case centre line takes precedence. Also for regular boundary line between two portions of a complete view.
(6) Irregular boundary line.

Right: 1953
(A) Continuous line (thick)–Visible outlines.
(B) Continuous line (thin)–Dimension lines. Projections or extension lines. Hatching or sectioning. Leader lines for notes. Outlines of revolved sections.

176

Similar steps were taken also in America although there the first national drawing standard was somewhat later in emerging. The American Society of Mechanical Engineers (founded in 1885) had already shown some interest in this matter and an ASME standard on cross-sections for drawings had been produced in 1914. In 1925 ASME and the Society for the Promotion of Engineering Education approached the American Standards Committee, later to become the American Standards Association. The organisational meeting of this committee was held in September 1926 and subsequently a questionnaire was circulated among industry to determine existing practice. The first standard was not approved, however, until 1935; it was revised in 1946 and again, in sections, from 1958 onwards.

Today, great effort is being put into the project of producing a comprehensive American Drafting Standards Manual. When finished this 360-page book will contain sections on:

(1) Size and Format
(2) Line Conventions, Sectioning and Lettering
(3) Projections
(4) Pictorial Drawing
(5) Dimensioning and Notes
(6) Screw Threads
(7) Gears, Splines and Serrations
(8) Castings
(9) Forgings
(10) Metal Stampings
(11) Plastics
(12) Die Castings
(13) Springs, Helical and Flat
(14) Structural Drafting
(15) Electrical Diagrams
(16) Tools, Dies and Gauges
(17) Fluid Power Diagrams

On top of these standards, known as ASA Y14-1, ASA Y14-2 and so on, there are a vast number of Military Standards in operation concerning the drawing field, such as:

MIL-STD-1B   General Drawing Practice
MIL-STD-2B   Engineering Drawings, Sizes and Formats
MIL-STD-7A   Types and Definitions of Engineering Drawings
MIL-STD-8C   Dimensioning and Tolerancing, etc.

(C) Short dashes (thin)—Hidden details. Portions to be removed.
(D) Long chain line (thin)—Centre lines. Path lines for indicating movement.
(E) Long chain line (thick)—Cutting or viewing planes.
(F) Short chain line (thin)—Developed or false views. Adjacent parts. Feature located in front of a cutting plane. Alternative positions of movable part.
(G) Continuous wavy (thick)—Irregular boundary lines. Short break lines.
(H) Ruled line and short zig-zags—Long break lines.

The standards position seems rather more complex in America than in most other countries, but this is because the term drafting is not synonymous with drawing and embraces all kinds of documentary and organisational matters concerning drawings. Why organisational matters come into the picture may be gauged from the fact that in 1960 the u.s. Military Services were estimated to have spent $1,500 million, or £535 million, on drafting and another third of this amount on reproduction of drawings.

The British drawing standard was born in similar circumstances, and the Explanatory Note to the original 1927 edition read as follows:

> The question of the Standardization of Drawing Office Practice concerns every branch of the Engineering Industry so that when a request was received from a Government Department that this work be undertaken by the British Engineering Standards Association, it was found that a number of the existing Sectional Committees were directly interested in the question. It was therefore decided to set up a Committee to prepare proposals for consideration by the Government Departments, Educational Bodies, Associations and Industrial Organisations interested in Engineering Drawing, and to submit the resulting recommendations for the consideration and approval of the various Sectional Committees of this Association. . . .
>
> This Committee early decided that before making any recommendations it would be necessary to ascertain as far as possible what was the general practice and for this purpose a Questionnaire was circulated. . . .
>
> The recommendations are made after careful consideration of the advice and remarks offered by the firms and Associations consulted. The work has been undertaken in the hope that some progress may be made towards that uniformity of practice which is so much to be desired, even at the expense of some change on the part of those whose present practice differs from that recommended. . . .
>
> Many conventions peculiar to individual industries have not been included as it was thought undesirable to incorporate details which might have a restrictive effect on the adoption of the recommendations generally.
>
> In view of the diversity of practice which exists in different firms and industries, the Committee are not recommending the adoption in all cases of hard and fast rules, but have included alternatives, and it is recognised that there will be a transition period before all the conventions recommended can be generally adopted.[82]

The recommendations ran to nearly three pages with one sheet of diagrams. To those who are familiar with a modern drawing standard, this might appear to be a very puny result from such a vast effort. It does, however, reflect the times and difficulties. A standard is, by its nature, a gathering together of the best common practice for the benefit of all. The smallness of this standard shows how little practice was common; apart from this the demands upon engineering drawings were not as stringent as they are today.

The Standard dealt with a number of points; with respect to aspects already discussed we may note the following recommendations:

COLOUR OF LINES

The use of colours should be avoided as far as possible. When colours are used, centre lines should be Brown, and dimension lines Blue with Black arrowheads and figures.

Note: To facilitate reproduction by photoprinting, Brown should be used instead of Red and a mixture of Prussian Blue and Chinese White should be used for the Blue.

INDICATION OF MATERIALS ON DRAWINGS

In view of the large variety of materials used, it is undesirable to rely on the various conventions of cross hatching except in the cases of wood and concrete. . . .

It is therefore recommended that in every case different materials should be indicated by notes on drawings and tracings. Any special means (e.g. hatching or colours) used to indicate different materials to be shown by a note or in a key diagram on the drawing or tracing.[82]

The American Drawing Standard ASA Z14-1, on the other hand, gave recommended sectioning practice for engineering drawings. This was not so much a retrograde step as a recognition that many materials other than metals were coming into use, such as rubber and plastics.

The preferred method of projection was naturally an item to be considered when the first British Standard on drawing practice was introduced. Now this particular convention has been a sore point over the years and a brief history can be seen by examining Fig. 71. The left views, taken from the 1927 standard, demonstrate first the projection recommended, First Angle, then the alternative which was to be marked clearly with the words 'Third Angle Projection', and lastly what to do if a mixed projection had to be used; the odd view was to be pointed out by using arrows to show the direction of viewing. In 1943 First Angle Projection was still the recommended standard, and if Third or Mixed Angle Projections were used the directions of viewing were to be clearly shown by arrows.

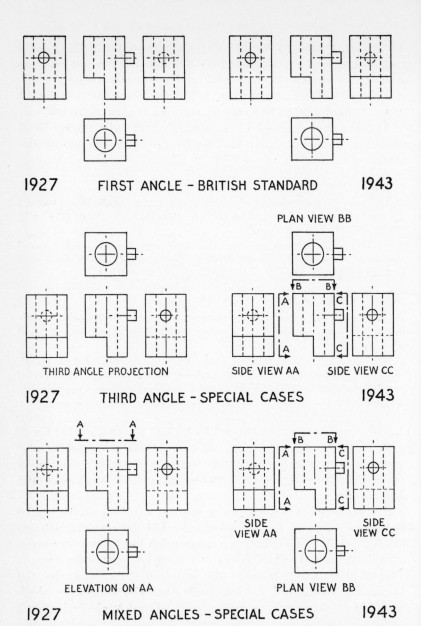

1927   FIRST ANGLE – BRITISH STANDARD   1943

PLAN VIEW BB

THIRD ANGLE PROJECTION   SIDE VIEW AA   SIDE VIEW CC

1927   THIRD ANGLE – SPECIAL CASES   1943

SIDE VIEW AA   SIDE VIEW CC

ELEVATION ON AA   PLAN VIEW BB

1927   MIXED ANGLES – SPECIAL CASES   1943

Fig. 71. Arrangement of views as given in successive British Standards. In all cases illustrated First Angle was the standard. In 1927 if Third Angle was used it had to be labelled thus. In 1943 this labelling disappeared and was replaced by arrows giving direction of viewing. In 1948 the 1927 principle was reverted to, while since then both First and Third have been standard, each being labelled accordingly.

The war years, however, had their effect as always, and after 1945 there was some pressure by the Armed Services to line up British practice with that of the u.s.a. and Canada. The first sign of this was the introduction of an amendment to the 1943 standard in 1948, which brought back the 1927 Third Angle Projection as an alternative. When the standard was completely revised in 1953, both First and Third Angle Projection were put on an equal footing and it was recommended that drawings should be marked to show which arrangement was being used.

Since then another amendment has been issued and the Services have stipulated that Third Angle Projection shall be used for all drawings applicable to the Services even if they are used mainly by industry. In the 1961 draft revision of B.S. 308 circulated for comment, the trend was made quite clear.

Two systems of projection are in use known respectively as First Angle and Third Angle, and both are acceptable as British Standards. In the interests of ultimate standardisation on one system only it is recommended that, wherever convenient, the third angle system of projection be adopted.

In view of the increasing co-operation between British and European industry, it seems unlikely that industry in Britain will wish to adopt any one system to the exclusion of the other.

This process of 'pushing' industrial practice in a particular direction over a number of years through a succession of small changes in a national standard, is worthy of note. Standards, as a rule, are just a solidification of existing practice. The British Engineering Drawing Practice Standard has been used since the last war in a new way – to lead industry by giving recommendations for practices, some of which were hardly used by industry but which technological progress would soon need. This particularly applied to dimensioning and tolerancing, where a clear lead was given to industry before technological circumstances forced various companies to adopt their own domestic methods.

This particular aspect will be dealt with in the next chapter, but we may note here that this more general process of leading rather than lagging has been carried on to some extent in the international sphere of standardisation. In the background is the International Organisation for Standardisation (ISO), and, working within this framework, is the ABC Group through which delegates from America, Britain and Canada endeavour to reconcile the standards of the three countries.

The ABC Group Committees tend to think of their work as one of 'unification' rather than 'standardisation'; what they decide cannot be forced upon any national standardisation body–they can only hope by compromise to seek the one best engineering answer and hope that their arguments and the standing of the persons concerned will lead the national committees to follow their lead.

Standardisation, of course, deals very largely with conventions. There are far too many conventions in the field of engineering drawing for many of them to be mentioned here. Most of them, like the V-thread of Fig. 72, have moved through various stages of

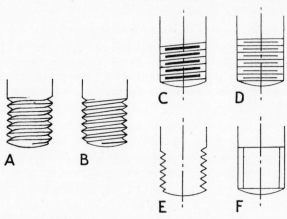

Fig. 72. Progressive simplification of the representation of screw threads from true projection in A to the purely symbolic in D and F.

simplification. As we saw in the early chapters a picture is a representation of something, and the representation need only be adequate for its function. Since threads, for example, are completely defined in various standards, there is no need for a drawing to show anything more than that there *is* a thread at a particular place–and suitable words or a code number will show exactly what kind of thread it is. Followed through, this practice leads naturally to a trend in recent years for simplified or functional draughting.

Simplified draughting has been preached mainly in the U.S.A. where it has been practised in a number of the larger organisations. The essential techniques were eventually published as a whole in 1953 in a book by Healy and Rau called *Simplified Drafting Practice*. When this work was issued there was a considerable opposition voiced through correspondence in the technical press. The general theme was that it was far more desirable that all drawings in a country – and if possible internationally – should be made to a common standard, than that some companies should make marginal savings in draughting time to the detriment of everyone else. It seems, however, that people were taken in by the title and the general philosophy expounded, rather than the substance of the book for, leaving aside special methods of reproduction, the use of photography and so on, the actual simplifications put forward were only marginally in advance of much general practice and many were only more complex applications of principles already sanctioned in national drawing standards.

Indeed, simplification is an inevitable trend in drawing as more and more items, which had previously to be manufactured, become stock items bought 'off the shelf'. When something is already in existence or already adequately defined, it is only necessary on a drawing to indicate its position in outline, or by a symbol – it depends upon the scale and purpose of the drawing. This has already led to extensive simplification in the drawing of gears, ball and roller bearings, valves and so on.

Symbols are a further stage of simplification which are useful in seeing an arrangement or system at a high level of abstraction. Possibly the use of electricity started the modern trend of using symbols, for this broke away from the machines and structures which made up the bulk of 19th-century engineering, and introduced what today we would recognise as systems engineering. Electrical arrangements called for the incorporation of a number of 'simple' items in a circuit, the true geometrical shape of which was almost immaterial. Initially these elements were switches, lamps, morse-keys, motors and solenoids, to be progressively built upon as many other inventions, such as selsyns and amplidyne generators, became standard items. A further subdivision occurred with the invention of radio, when various kinds of tubes (valves), capacitors, inductors, resistors and transformers became the building bricks.

We are lucky today in that through the various national standardisation bodies an attempt is usually made to recommend acceptable symbols for any emerging technology before individuals are led to invent their own different symbols. As well as those for electrical and electronic engineering, there are now symbols for piping, especially steam piping, and fluid power – hydraulic and pneumatic systems – oil and chemical plant and much else.

A typical use of symbols in circuitry drawing work is shown in Fig. 73–in this case part of an electrical circuit and valves in hydraulic lines.

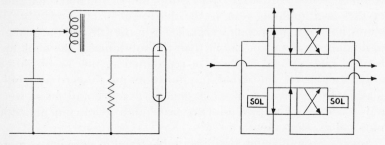

HIGH PRESSURE MERCURY
ARC VAPOUR LAMP CIRCUIT

SOLENOID CONTROLLED PILOT
VALVE OPERATING MACHINE
CONTROL VALVE

Fig. 73. Parts of an electrical circuit and a hydraulic system depicted in symbolic terms.

Symbolism of this sort is of more than passing interest, for if one thinks about it carefully one can see it as a replacement of drawings defining objects in terms of real or apparent shapes with drawings which are simple representations of essential characteristics. Indeed, it is the modern counterpart of the cave drawing shown in Fig. 8.

16

Defining Shape : Dimensioning
and Tolerancing

DRAWING standards over the years, and especially those of different countries, have varied quite considerably. Some, like the first British drawing standard, have been concise and concerned only with broad principles; others, such as the Australian standard, have grown into large reference works, covering all manner of drawing practices at great length over all engineering fields, often including building drawing practice as well.

When the British Standard 308 was revised in 1953, however, it was unique amongst all the varied drawing standards—it broke new ground and the material contained therein has become the basis for most other modern drawing standards. The changes were recorded in the Foreword to the new standard as follows:

The most important changes concern the section on Dimensioning and Tolerancing, which has been greatly amplified in the light of valuable experience gathered during the intervening years. In other respects, the section on General Practice has been confined to recommended principles and methods to be followed in the preparation of engineering drawings. Subjects such as architectural drawings, survey plans, graphs, drawing reproduction, and the nature and handling of drawing materials have been excluded, as it is considered that such matters are more fully and more appropriately dealt with in other British Standards.[84]

The title was changed from *Engineering Drawing Office Practice* to *Engineering Drawing Practice* to match the change in contents. As was mentioned in the last chapter, the real, more subtle, change in this standard was that it did not represent a condensation of current British industrial practice, but gave, and was intended to give, a lead to the engineering world.

Today, modern methods of dimensioning and tolerancing are bound up in some people's minds with the idea of interchangeability. This view is unnecessarily restrictive and has arisen through the history of events rather than from an objective rational standpoint. To put it most simply, systematic dimensioning and tolerancing on drawings is necessary in any situation where design and manufacture are completely separated, so that parts can be made from the information given on drawings and assembled without the need for 'fitting', 'offering up' or such like. This, of course, can apply to the one-off job just as much as to the mass-produced article. However, the history of engineering has tended to obscure this simple view.

From the time of Plato onwards it was recognised, consciously by the philosophers and perhaps unconsciously by the artisans, that whereas geometry was precise and exact, mechanics was not, for whereas geometry dealt with ideal abstractions, nobody could construct a perfect line, plane or other geometrical shape in or on material. In the world of craftsmanship this did not matter very much. For instance, it is unlikely that the parts of the Trevithick valve shown in Fig. 69 were drawn separately. Since it was only the total valve which was required and one man would make all of it, one drawing of the whole was sufficient and no dimensions were added in terms of figures. The essential sizes could be taken off the drawing with proportional dividers – without invoking any units of measurement – and it would not matter very much whether they were strictly adhered to or not. The craftsman was aware of the function of the valve and so long as the parts fitted properly all was well. He would make the valve body and the valve plugs as best he could, then he would file, scrape or grind in these parts until the internal and external tapered parts showed a sufficiently close match.

If it were necessary to make a number of such valves and to make the valve bodies and valve plugs separately, this could be done by first making a taper plug and bore gauge. The man making the valve bodies would then make all his tapers to fit the plug gauge, while the man making the valve plugs would make them to fit the ring or bore gauge.

In principle this is exactly what happened in the story of mass-production. Most early mass-production of precision items – as opposed to that of buttons, pins, etc. – took place in America, notably in the manufacture of guns and clocks. The principle of interchangeability of parts was used in these two fields for two distinct reasons. Where guns were concerned, it was for the benefit of the user, so that weapons could be kept serviceable by replacing broken parts without having to call on the services of a craftsman. In the clock industry, interchangeability was mainly a benefit to the manufacturer, in that all like parts were so alike that assembly needed only unskilled labour.

Interchangeability, however, did not come about through the medium of drawings; instead it was largely through the provision of gauges and templates. Initially some of the methods were rather crude, such as filing pieces clamped between contoured, hardened jaws–a process which was rough on the files and the contoured jaws. Later this gave way to the principle of manufacturing like parts on the same machine, with the same tools, set-up, jigs, etc., and the checking of parts with master gauges.

In 1815, in America, it was hoped to produce muskets in a number of different armouries, government and private, such that all would be standard with interchangeable parts. As we have seen, at the time this could not be done by distributing drawings; instead, a number of 'perfect' muskets were made according to master gauges and jigs, and these were sent to the various armouries with the instruction that 'no deviations from the pattern were to be allowed'. These armouries then had the job of making their own gauges, jigs, etc., from the patterns supplied and all the parts would then be manufactured with the aid of this equipment. On the whole the system worked. In 1824 a hundred rifles from different armouries were taken to pieces, mixed in a pile and then reassembled at random. In 1853 the British Small Arms Commission, of which Sir Joseph Whitworth was a member, recommended the Government to introduce 'The American System' for interchangeable manufacture.[61]

The point of this short dissertation is to show that mass-production could be, and was, effected without any call upon drawings, for the simple reason that, at that time, drawings were inadequate for this purpose. The proper place of engineering drawings in the scheme of things was, however, recognised in some quarters, at least in principle.

Ferdinand Redtenbacher, in 1852, wrote these very prophetic words:

Drawing is a means by which the mechanical engineer can represent his thoughts and ideas with a clarity and distinctness that leave nothing to be desired. A machine that has been drawn is like an ideal realisation of it, but in a material that costs little and is easier to handle than iron and steel.

To draw a machine requires an expenditure of time and effort incomparably less than that needed to build the machine in iron and steel, especially if one considers the usefulness of the drawing both for the plan and its execution.

If everything is first well thought out, and the essential dimensions determined by calculation or experience, the plan of a machine or installation of machines can be quickly put on paper and the whole thing as well as the detail can then most conveniently be submitted to the severest criticism. If the whole is found to be unsatisfactory, the drawing is discarded and a second, better one is soon ready. If only certain changes of detail are desirable or necessary, the parts to be changed can be readily removed and replaced by others that are better. If at first there is doubt as to which of various possible arrangements is the most desirable then they are all sketched, compared with one another, and the most suitable can easily be chosen.

But drawings are of the utmost importance not only in planning but also for execution, since by means of them the measurements and proportions of all the parts can be so sharply and definitely determined from the beginning that when it comes to manufacture it is only necessary to imitate in the materials used for construction exactly what is shown in the drawing. Every part of the machine can in general be manufactured independently of every other part; it is therefore possible to distribute the entire work among a great number of workers, and to organise the whole business of manufacture in such a manner that each job can be completed at the right time, in the most suitable position, with the least expenditure of time, money and material, and with an accuracy and reliability which leave almost nothing to be desired. No substantial errors can arise in work organized in this manner, and if it does happen that on a rare occasion a mistake has been made, it is immediately known with whom the blame lies.[59]

In these paragraphs Redtenbacher describes the place and use of drawings in engineering very clearly. His ideas fall into two natural parts. The first deals with drawing as an instrument for design–imitating real objects on paper so that they can be assessed and any judged failings or incompatibilities smoothed out by changes –and his 'ideal realisation' expresses the abstractness of these drawings. The second part deals with drawings as a means of communicating to considerable numbers of people what they are required to make.

However, as we have already seen with reference to the valve drawing, the mere provision of outlines on paper is insufficient. The mass-production line of thought led to gauges and similar equipment to make good the deficiency. There was, however, another line of development which was concerned with the breakdown of the manufacture of parts–first between workshops, then between firms and, ultimately, between factories in different countries. Instead of providing the actual equipment to copy–as was done with rifles—parts represented in drawings could be further defined by giving the actual dimensions and angles in terms of figures.

This, of course, entailed two further requirements: suitable measuring equipment and standards of measurement. Indeed, without advances in the science of metrology, engineering could never have progressed to its present state, and all subsequent improvements in the definition of parts in engineering drawings are based on the assumption that measuring equipment is available.

Changes were, nevertheless, slow and dependent upon contemporary demands. A further advance is shown in Fig. 74. By the middle of the 19th century engineering workshops had taken on the form we now call 'jobbing shops'. In most cases the early types of machine tools would be arranged along either side of the shop under the windows. Quite often the machine being made was assembled—or more properly, built—in the centre of the shop floor. In consequence the mechanics were quite familiar with the processes involved and the functions of the various parts, and a great deal was left to their discretion. Although dimensions are given in Fig. 74, these are what we would call today 'design sizes'. There is, however, better definition; the taper on the Gib is additionally defined as 'Taper of Gib $\frac{1}{4}$ of an inch to the foot', for example. The number of threads per inch is also given in figures.

At a later stage, especially as machines, mechanisms and parts increasingly unfamiliar to the craftsmen were being defined, the various parts were drawn out as separate items, the basic dimensions being supplemented by the addition of the terms 'Running Fit', 'Sliding Fit', 'Press Fit', etc., often abbreviated to R.F., S.F. and P.F. The assembly of the parts was effected by making available to the machinists standard plug and ring gauges and thread gauges, although invariably some final fitting or selective assembly was required.

Although it was probably not very apparent at the time, these facilities and additional methods of definition were bringing into being a split between design and manufacture and this was particularly so in one special quarter. The largest consumers of engineering products without manufacturing facilities of their own were, and still are, the Armed Services. Being concerned with national security, secrecy of intention was often most important and this led to splitting up projects amongst very many firms. Even when secrecy was not the aim the sheer mass of material required meant employing many manufacturers to produce it. The Armed Services

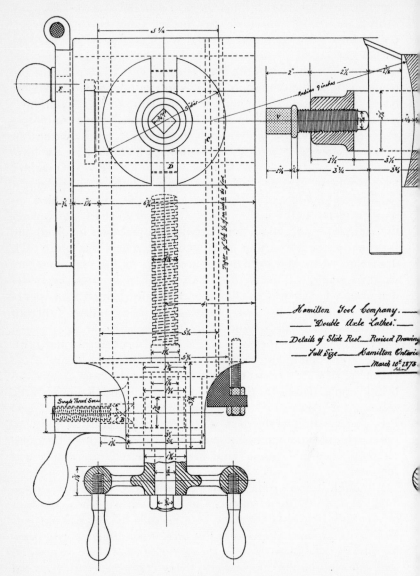

Fig. 74. Copy of an old drawing marked 'Hamilton Tool Company–Double Axle Lathes–Details of Slide Rest–Revised Drawing June 17/78–Full Size–Hamilton Ontario–March 10th 1878'. No further detail drawings would be made and the machine builders worked from this one copy. The irregular section lining was

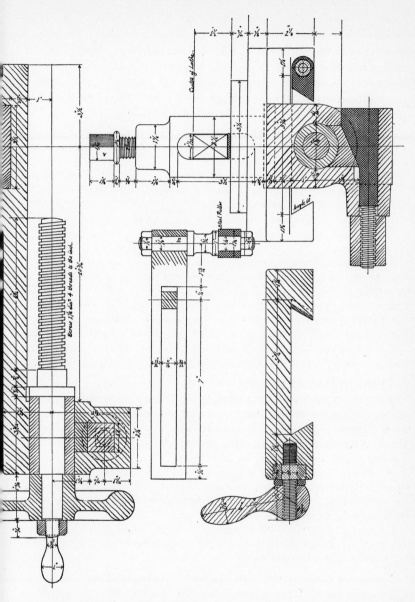

done freehand with a brush using a medium density water colour. In this copy
these lines have been made thinner than in the original but the overall density
and appearance is the same.

have, therefore, always been pioneers in improving engineering practice. The first British drawing standard, as we have seen, came into being at the request of the Armed Services as a result of experience gained in the 1914–18 war. In much the same way further shortcomings came to light in the 1939–45 war, which resulted in the publication of a, then, unique work called *Dimensional Analysis of Engineering Designs*, the Foreword of which said:

This publication is the work of an Inter-Services Committee set up at a Conference held on 24th October 1944, by the Ministry of Production with the following terms of reference:

(a) To establish for Armament work a basic system for tolerancing and dimensioning Drawings of Stores, Gauges, Jigs and Fixtures of various degrees of precision.

(b) To make recommendations as to how the principles and practice so established can be made known to and applied by the Engineering Industry.

The Committee have interpreted 'Armament Work' in the widest possible sense, and in consequence the present volume is believed to be generally applicable to all engineering practice. . . . The work of this Committee has been based to a large extent on that of an earlier Admiralty Committee set up in 1942 to revise the basis for the preparation of torpedo drawings, the outcome of which was the issue by the Admiralty of two comprehensive Manuals entitled 'Data Sheets for Designers and Draughtsmen, Vol. 1, Part 1–Components; Vol. 1, Part 2–Gauges. . . .'

From the Introduction we read:

Some engineers who have had bitter experience of the many difficulties attending the production, inspection and servicing of new designs have come to regard this state of affairs as inevitable, but it is certain that many of these difficulties which are at present solved by such laborious and expensive methods, can be avoided in the early stages of design. In many cases the troubles of production, inspection and servicing can be tracked down to their source in the engineering drawings of the production design, and are generally attributable to either one or the other or both of the following causes:

(1) Incorrect analysis of the dimensional requirements of the design, and

(2) Incorrect, ambiguous or incomplete statement of the requirements on the engineering drawing. . . .[81]

The work quoted dealt, on the whole, with the dimensional requirements in different cases, and the revised drawing standard B.S. 308 of 1953 dealt substantially with the complete statement of the requirements on engineering drawings, although naturally there was an area of overlap.

What, in fact, was happening was that design and production

were becoming more and more divorced as two different functions, whilst the link between them—the drawings mainly—was inadequate. The simple idea of tolerancing was well known, but this generally meant merely quoting a minimum and maximum size which was considered to be acceptable. However, even using tolerancing, standard gauges and precision measuring equipment, delivered parts did not always carry out their functions or even fit where they were intended.

The reason was that drawings were still largely representations of the ideal, although they might specify some variations in sizes. Two holes might be bored at either end of a component, both being checked for size very accurately with the sizes given on the drawing —yet they might prove to be not quite on the same centre-line and unacceptable. Sometimes a face might not be quite square to another face or axis. The trouble was that sometimes these things did not matter and sometimes they did, but in both cases they were represented on the drawings by an abstraction with no indication of what variation from the ideal could be tolerated.

Simple tolerancing, in principle, gave in certain instances virtually two forms for a component—a maximum and minimum shape within which the real component's shape should lie. Whilst in principle this is sound and easy to grasp, in practice it was insufficient for definition. This can be shown by the diagrams in Fig. 75. Suppose a piece is drawn and dimensioned as in (a), this could be interpreted as in (b). The angle in the latter is some way out of the square—it has a slope of 0·010 in. in the piece width—whilst the face concerned lies within the specified sizes. This might prove to be acceptable, in which case nothing more need be said. However, the squareness of the faces might be important and the 'new geometry' allows us additionally to define this through the concept shown in (c). Here two parallel planes 0·005 in. apart and perpendicular to the face A are specified and the whole of the upright face must lie between these planes. This is specified on the drawing as in (d). The original tolerance on the length of face A is retained, but the squareness of the two faces is additionally defined. Left like this the upright face could have any surface which fell between the two specified planes—concave, convex or wavy—and this might be acceptable. If it is not, then the flatness required can also be separately defined by stating, for example, 'Flat Tol. 0·002 in. Wide'. In short, it is possible to superimpose a number of tolerances upon one another, each concerned with a different quality.

o   193

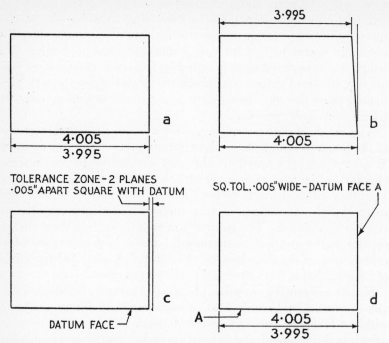

Fig. 75. Illustrating the superimposition of a squareness tolerance upon a dimensional tolerance. Other tolerances, such as one for flatness, could also be superimposed.

Fig. 76 shows how these new ideas have changed the look of engineering drawings. (a) is a drawing of a part made about 1920; all the sizes given are 'ideal' and this part would be fitted to other components as they were being manufactured, hence the note '1¼ in. Dia. Bore R.F. on Spindle C'.

The same part, still being produced as a spare, is shown in (b) taken from a 1956 drawing which uses the new dimensioning methods; the two bores not only have tolerances on their sizes, but a special note defines their concentricity one to another. The squareness of the left-hand face is also specified by a note. In theory the whole form could be completely specified by means of appropriate tolerancing, but in practice a lot is still left to what might be called 'normal engineering practice'. For instance, one could specify the concentricity of all the external turned parts, whereas, in fact, only the concentricity of the two bores is quoted. Normally it can be taken for granted that a manufacturer will turn and bore as

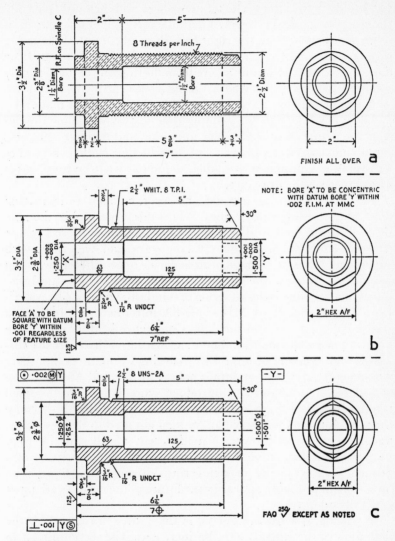

Fig. 76. Changes in drawing practice from 1920 to 1961.
 (a) Original drawing, 1920.
 (b) Same item re-drawn in 1956 to the then current Canadian Standard.
 (c) Re-drawn in terms of current Canadian Standard with symbols replacing notes. The symbols for 'diameter' and 'reference' dimension are international.

many surfaces as he can at one setting—indeed, in this case it might be possible to turn the whole lot in this way and then just 'part off' the complete piece. However, a manufacturer might machine most of the component from the right end, then take it out of the lathe, turn it round and complete the machining from the left end. If he does do this, he is now quite aware from the drawing of the accuracy required and can decide whether using a self-centring chuck will be sufficient or whether the piece should be mounted on a mandrel.

These new methods for defining practical shapes allow the designer to define on paper his true intentions and requirements, and the manufacturer can then use any production method he wishes according to equipment available, so long as what he turns out is as specified on the drawings.

The new tolerancing methods, however, entailed an increasing amount of wording on drawings. Whilst this was not objectionable in itself, it did tend to defeat somewhat its own purpose because different countries have different languages, and even those with superficially the same language often decide upon different wording of notes according to the national usage of words. The natural way out of this difficulty is the adoption of standard symbols. The American Military Standard MIL-STD-8A introduced symbols for a trial some years ago and the ABC Conference held in Toronto in 1957 discussed this matter. The u. k. delegation had already discussed such symbols with the ISO Working Committees and there was general agreement on future policy. Britain and America then considered it premature to introduce symbols into the national standards—although these were bound to come—partly because they did not think industry had by then got used to the new tolerancing methods. However, Canada went ahead and in 1959 published the first standard containing symbols for position and geometrical tolerancing on engineering drawings. Fig. 76 (c) shows how (b) will probably appear in the future as the symbols are more generally adopted.

In passing, it is worth noticing in these three drawings how the definition of the threads has also increased. The section-lining in (a) is a carry-over from the days of coloured drawings and was used to represent brass and bronze parts.

The late George Noble had this to say at the time the new Canadian Drawing Standard was introduced:

. . . the whole object of symbolization . . . is to establish world-wide use of the absolute minimum of simple, positive, ideographic symbols in order to ensure that the design requirements are clearly evident to the reader without recourse to any interpretation, linguistic or otherwise. The introduction of the symbol system . . . also conforms to the modern trend for simplified or functional drawing practice and represents a logical development of the drawing symbols included in many standards in recent years. For example, welding symbols, symbols for screw-threads, symbols for surface finish and the like. . . .

This new and vital step towards unification and simplification brings us still closer to the goal of the ABC movement. This goal can be simply defined as–the production of engineering drawings throughout the Western World which will convey the complete design requirements for interchangeability of manufacture in any country regardless of the languages or customs of this country or the country of origin. If a drawing can be interpreted and interchangeable parts correctly manufactured when all communications with the office of origin are completely cut off, then we will have achieved the goal of the Unified Standards programme.[55]

17

Axonometric Projection

MULTI-VIEW orthographic projections necessarily became the standard medium for engineering drawings, because one could only design in terms of true shape, and one could only truly and unambiguously record shape in this way. But multi-view drawings have always been difficult to interpret at first sight. Monge and many others recognised this and postulated colouring and shadows to assist in interpretation. Farish also saw this difficulty and put forward his isometrical perspective.

Since this business of interpretation is an inherent difficulty there have been attempts to overcome it throughout modern engineering history, the most successful being those generally classed loosely as axonometric projections. In past years the term 'axonometric' has been used in various countries and by different professions to mean different things. However, we shall consider it in its modern meaning as that sort of drawing resulting from a projection which shares the properties of both perspective and orthographic projections. It portrays objects in terms of apparent shapes, yet it is an orthographic projection on to one plane. It has the best, or worst, of both systems according to one's viewpoint.

A brief history of axonometric projection, at least in terms of principles, is not only of interest in itself but it tends to throw into sharp focus the different philosophies which lie behind technical drawing on the Continent, in Britain and in America.

Farish's isometric drawing was a special case of axonometric projection, and as British orthographic projection distilled itself into a series of drawing axioms, it became fashionable to derive the isometric cube through these axioms. Fig. 77 (a) shows how this was done. Although the layout is somewhat different, this is fundamentally the same as Binns's drawing in Fig. 55. Starting at the top with two true shape views—a plan and elevation—one is rotated through a 45-degree position so that an auxiliary view may be projected from it. This auxiliary view is then tilted appropriately so that a second auxiliary view—the isometric cube—can be projected.

The same projection techniques can be used, of course, with

arbitrary angles of rotation and tilt as in Fig. 77 (b), the last view being the axonometric one. Although only cubes are used to illustrate the principles, naturally more complex shapes can be dealt with by similar methods.

Whilst such projections were useful as school exercises, the method was too tedious for practical use, particularly as it meant using an auxiliary view which had to be constructed separately and might become very complicated though it was ultimately redundant. One way out of this was to get away from projection and stick to 'secondary geometries'. In the case of the isometric position

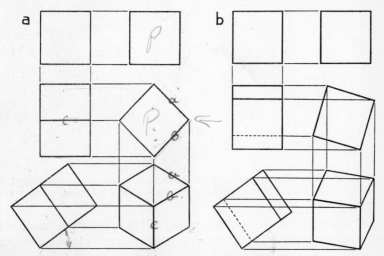

Fig. 77. *Left*, an isometric cube, and *right*, a tri-metric cube, both derived from the classical solid geometry or orthographic projection approach.

this could be accomplished by using a 30-degree set-square and an isometric scale for measurements along the isometric axes (0·816 true size). In a similar way, a position such as that of the cube in Fig. 77 (b) could be taken as standard, whereupon a special template could be manufactured as in Fig. 78. Objects to be illustrated would be measured on the engineering drawings in terms of lengths, widths and heights and these would be placed into the axonometric drawing by using the appropriate scales on the template's edges. Drawings made in this way were sometimes called 'tri-metric' because they had three scales, one for each axis. Special positions could also be chosen so that the scales of two axes were the same; there being only two scales then, the term 'di-metric' was used.

Special templates of this kind became commercially available in Britain during the Second World War. Up to this time there was little interest by British draughtsmen in pictorial drawing methods. They had been brought up through apprenticeships and were expected to have engineering 'know-how' rather than pure drawing ability. The technological nature of the last war, however, forced many persons into industry who were quite ungrounded in engineering, and an interest grew in supplementing multi-view orthographic drawings with pictorial views—for which purpose axometric projections were excellent.

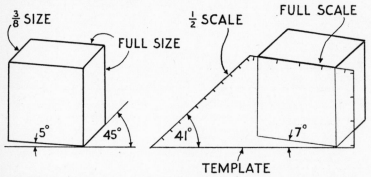

Fig. 78. Using a template with three engraved scales to make an axonometric drawing without resorting to projection. Two standard 'di-metric' cubes are shown.

Whilst there was a lot of experimentation and various methods were taken up by a few companies, this interest reached its peak only after the war had ended, by which time it seemed that the situation would revert to normal and supplementary pictures would not be required. Most British draughtsmen were pleased with this trend—having been raised as engineers they disliked any attempt to turn them into 'artists'. Chief draughtsmen were also pleased because skilled drawing-office labour had become very scarce and they disliked not only their staffs 'wasting time' on 'pretty pictures', but also the time lost in training them for this work. Many persons misread the signs at the time and a number of interesting books appeared offering new methods.

Drawings based on a secondary geometry call for an initial special arrangement to be analysed into co-ordinates, that is, translated into figures and directions, and then to be re-translated into another geometrical arrangement. The co-ordination between a point in the original orthographic views and the axonometric view is a mental one–and a draughtsman can often make mistakes in this translation. The draughtsman naturally prefers a drawing system comparable to that which he normally uses, one in which a point in one view has a projectional relationship with the same point exhibited in another view. Although there was a good case, therefore, to develop a 'pure' drawing system for making axonometric views quickly and, as far as possible, 'mechanically' to avoid errors of translation, some persons went to the opposite extreme and proposed systems which used a series of printed tables whereby by looking up given axes' angles and lengths, the axonometric angles and lengths could be read off. It was through being asked to help with the compilation of such tables that W. E. Walters evolved his own method published as *Three-Dimensional Engineering Drawing* in 1949.

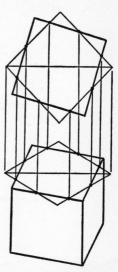

He recognised that the easiest system to deal with from the drawing point of view was isometric, yet it appeared that greater flexibility was required. He combined the two very successfully by keeping one isometric axis fixed and moving the other two out of coincidence with the natural axes of the object to be depicted. This, in principle, had always been possible, for isometric drawing deals with points which can be measured from any arbitrary reference axes. In practice this meant that the plan of the object was rotated to the optimum position and a 'ghost' square was superimposed upon it at 45 degrees rotation as in Fig. 79. The isometric rhombus representing the square was drawn projectionally beneath the square, and the points where lines on the

Fig. 79. The basis of Walters's *Three-Dimensional Engineering Drawing* 1949. An axonometric drawing with 'isometric tilt' but variable 'rotation'.

plan crossed the rotated square were dropped into the rhombus and suitably joined up to give an 'isometric' view of the given plan in its selected position. The 'depths' were then added as in an ordinary isometric drawing by using an isometric scale (0·816 true size), since the vertical axis remained in coincidence with the object's natural vertical axis.

Notice that the methods so far described are based upon moving an object around, the plane of projection being considered fixed.

As an apprentice I was taught orthographic projection axioms through exercises similar to those of Fig. 77. I remember at the time thinking that there ought to be a direct projectional relationship between an axonometric view and the original orthographic outlines, and one day it came to me in a flash. The relationship was so ridiculously simple that I did not consider writing about it until prompted some years later. Looking at a drawing like Fig. 77 one noticed that the axonometric (or isometric) cube was projectionally in line with the rotated square. As all the cube's faces were identical a similar relationship must exist for all of them. An axonometric cube could be projected as shown in Fig. 80 directly from plan and

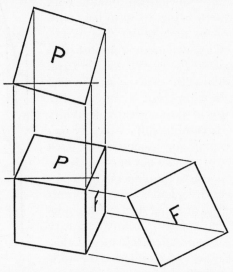

Fig. 80. The basis of Booker's *Direct Pictorial Projection* 1950.

elevation. What made this so interesting to me was that the two squares could be replaced by any two related orthographic outlines and the axonometric view projected with no further ado. Naturally, the positions of the original views and the slopes of the projectors need to be determined. The interested reader may deduce how this is done from the illustration, all the construction lines being shown.

This system of axonometric projection–as opposed to axonometric drawing–was published as a series of articles in 1949[10] It is noteworthy that this system was not derived from classical descriptive geometry principles, nor even really from the axioms of orthographic projection. It arose from that much earlier school of thinking in which views were lined up on paper as seemed most convenient.

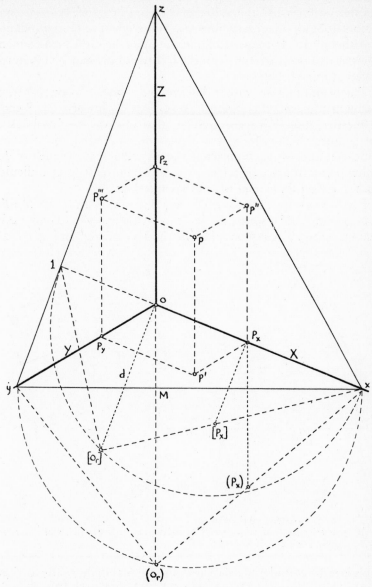

Fig. 81. The first illustration from Schuessler's *Orthogonale Axonometrie* 1905.

No attempt was made to explain the relationship between the ortho-graphic outlines and the axonometric view in terms of space pro-jectors from an imaginary object, as this seemed to be redundant.

Although I was unaware of it at the time, the same arrangement of views had been arrived at on the Continent through a very much different line of thought.

The beginnings are rather obscure, but a book was published in Berlin in 1905 called *Orthogonale Axonometrie*, written by Dr. Rudolf Schuessler, though it seems unlikely that this was the first book of this nature. Schuessler's system was derived from the classical Descartes and Monge approach and went back to the idea of de-fining points in space by reference to three mutually perpendicular planes, giving three axes where they intersect.

Fig. 81 is a copy of Schuessler's first diagram. This is rather diffi-cult to follow and quoting his accompanying text would only make matters worse. The essence of his method is extracted in Fig. 82 (a).

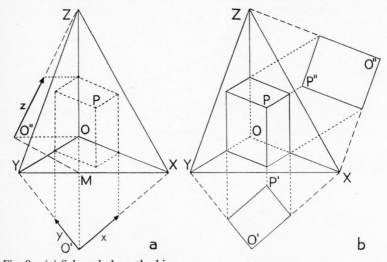

Fig. 82. (a) Schuessler's method in use.
(b) A development of (a) which Schuessler missed, but which was described by Schmid in 1922 and Eckhart in 1938.

This is to be considered as a view of three planes mutually at right angles with origin at O and axes OX, OY and OZ. The plane of projection, or the paper, cuts these three planes in the traces XY, YZ and ZX. The aim is to position a point in this view given its three co-ordinates x, y and z. The horizontal plane OXY is first revolved about the trace XY to give triangle $XO'Y$ its true shape. The co-ordinate distances x and y are then marked off from O' and projected vertically on to the axes OX and OY. To find the vertical position of the point, an imaginary plane at right angles to the paper passing through ZOM is revolved to give its true shape $ZO''M$. Co-ordinate distance z is then marked off from O'' and projected on to axis OZ. A series of parallel lines in the picture then intersect in point P, which is the axonometric position of the point with co-ordinates x, y, z. Every point required would be found in this way.

Although the method was tedious and complex, with patience it was possible to build up pictures of fairly complicated objects. Fig. 83 is a typical drawing exercise from Schuessler's book. Having produced the axonometric view of this piece of timber construction,

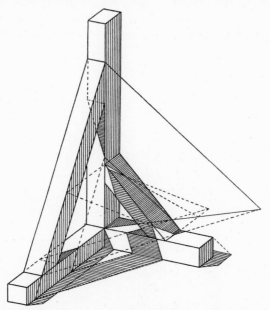

Fig. 83. A later exercise given in Schuessler's *Orthogonale Axonometrie* 1905. This may be considered to be the three-dimensional counterpart of the technique typified by Fig. 57.

the student was expected to carry out further geometrical constructions to define rigorously the shadows cast by the parts.

If anyone tried to explain such a method of drawing to today's technical students there would be little enthusiasm. In 1905 there was less to learn and more time for this sort of exercise.

It is of interest to note that if Schuessler had placed the plan of point *P* in the triangle *XO'Y* to give *P'* as in Fig. 82 (b) and then treated trace *XZ* (or *YZ*) analogously to trace *XY* he would have come to an arrangement very close to that of Fig. 80. The only difference is that Schuessler's plan and elevation would have been mirror images.

That he did not take these few extra steps was presumably because his education had put him into an orthodox groove. The relationship was, of course, seen later. The first treatment was probably that of Professor Theodor Schmid of Vienna, in his book *Darstellende Geometrie*; Vol. 1, *Orthogonale Axonometrie* of 1922. For some reason the work was forgotten until recently and the credit was given to Professor L. Eckhart, also of Vienna, who published a paper outlining the system of projection directly from plans and elevations in 1938[31]. The key diagram from this paper is given in Fig. 84. Notice its similarity to Schuessler's first diagram, and also

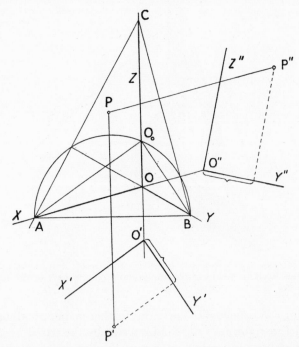

Fig. 84. The key figure in Eckhart's *Ein neues Schrägrissverfahren* 1938. Note similarity between this and Fig. 81, though the treatment is fairly abstract.

the philosophy of dealing with one point in isolation in an abstract setting. This is in contrast to the practice in Britain of dealing with solid geometry–attaching points, as it were, to solid figures. Both methods of presentation are the result of the roots of technical drawing being different as we have seen in earlier chapters.

Moving to America we find that Professors Randolph P. Hoelscher and Clifford C. Springer introduced this type of axonometric projection in their book *Engineering Drawing and Geometry* in 1956 and many other text-book writers followed suit. Although their ideas seem to have stemmed directly from Eckhart's paper, they were differently presented. The Americans had a peculiar advantage in demonstrating this relationship between standard orthographic and axonometric views. Being a country in which third angle projection was standard, the usual method of describing arrangements of plans and elevations was by use of the 'glass box' technique mentioned in Chapter 14. This technique could easily be modified to accommodate axonometric projection as a view on a second auxiliary plane. The 'box' could be opened out flat, each of the primary planes being revolved about hinges on the auxiliary plane as in Fig. 85.

The term axonometric projection seems to have a continental origin, but it is now generally accepted in America for this type of drawing. There is a tendency also to accept it in Britain, but the issue has been confused in the past because architects used the term to describe a form of planometric projection–oblique projection based on a plan instead of an elevation. To overcome this in 1912 it was suggested that a new name–axometric–should be adopted to cover iso-, di-, and tri-metric projections, the word 'axonometric' being used as a generic term to cover all kinds of pictorial projections which used, as a theoretical basis, parallel space projectors. This was revived in 1959.*

Although the projectional relationship between an axonometric view and the orthographic outlines was well established, there has remained a stumbling block which prevents this modern idea from being put to very much use. We have got so used to the conventional layout of technical drawings that we have tended to forget that it is only a convenient arrangement. Even if we have recognised this and considered the practical possibility of arranging orthographic

---

* See Trigg, C. F., 'Application of the Eccentric and True Anomalies of the Ellipse to Isometric and Axometric Projection', *Proc. I. Mech. E., London*, Vol. 173, No. 31, pp. 747–760. (1959), and Ref. 45 (1912).

views of an object around a central axonometric view, our drawing equipment is all right-angle based. To be of any real use either the new system had to be developed to be compatible with existing

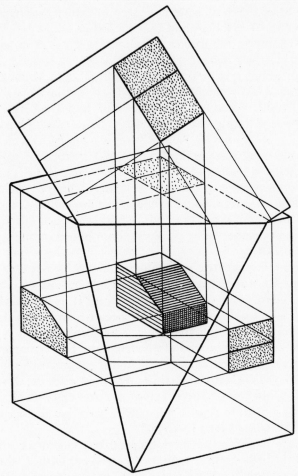

Fig. 85. Axonometric projection demonstrated in terms of the American 'Glass Box'.

equipment, or new equipment had to be devised and, in fact, both lines have been followed.

The first approach resulted from a proposal made by the author some years ago. In order to conform with conventional practice the original outlines used for projecting the axonometric view should be next to one another and in line. This could be accomplished as in Fig. 86. This is virtually Fig. 80 with the side elevation put back into its conventional position, taking the oblique projection lines with it. These are reconnected to the axonometric view by back-projecting via a reflecting line. In terms of classical descriptive geometry this reflecting line has no tangible existence, but it has at least one

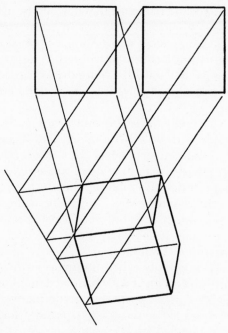

Fig. 86. Modification of direct projection as in Fig. 80. Projection is from original outlines in conventional positions via a reflecting line.

precedent–Dürer used one as shown in Fig. 23–as distinct from an ordinary mitre line. It is of considerable interest to compare this Figure with that of Fig. 77 (b) which accomplished the same result in rather more stages.

Once direct projection of axonometric views has been explained, like any good design it appears so obvious. Yet before its general promulgation a great many very intelligent persons who had given great thought to the matter completely missed the idea because they thought habitually in terms appropriate to their particular educational philosophy. For instance, Professor J. G. McGuire expounded *A New Approach to Axonometric Projection* in 1944[49];

however, it was a rediscovery of the layout shown in Fig. 61 from the 19th century.

The alternative approach, the devising of special drawing equipment, was tackled by Professor Wayne L. Shick, of the University of Illinois. In practice, axonometric views were generally projected from orthographic views which had been drawn conventionally and then separated for positioning on the drawing board. This had many disadvantages and it seemed that it would be more ideal if the orthographic views could easily be drawn in the correct positions for projecting an axonometric view. A number of experiments were put in hand, but using arbitrary 'tri-metric' positions created as many difficulties as they solved. Eventually he settled for the standard isometric position which led to a neat symmetrical arrangement.

The equipment finally devised is shown in Fig. 87. It consists of a triangular frame with 60-degree angles, and a special template or quadrangle. As can be seen, edges AB and BC relate like points in the plan and side elevation, the quadrangle sliding against side EF of the triangle. Edge AD relates points in the plan with their counterparts in the isometric view. Since the arrangement is symmetrical, the quadrangle can be used likewise against the other two sides of the triangle, as shown by the broken lines, thus connecting up all views with one another.

The system was originally called 'isometric-orthographic', then 'orthoisographic' and finally it was christened the 'United Drawing System'. It has been used experimentally in many American colleges and companies for some years, especially for teaching. In 1961 some large models with a triangle size of 42 in. edge were made for experimental use in a large American aircraft company works on production drawings.

The foregoing covers very briefly the general trends in the development of axonometric projection. There have, of course, been many variations on some of these themes, and it is not here suggested that any one method is universally best in any particular circumstances. We have simply focused our interest on clear lines of development.

Whilst oblique projection is generally discussed in modern textbooks under the heading of pictorial drawing, historically it has no projectional basis. Empirically based drawings of this nature – the box at the foot of Fig. 51 is an example of oblique projection – have been made for centuries. They stem from drawings like those of

Fig. 11. In Diderot's *Encyclopedia* there are innumerable examples, especially noteworthy being those depicting door locks and printers' type.

It was not until the text-book writers of the late 19th century felt

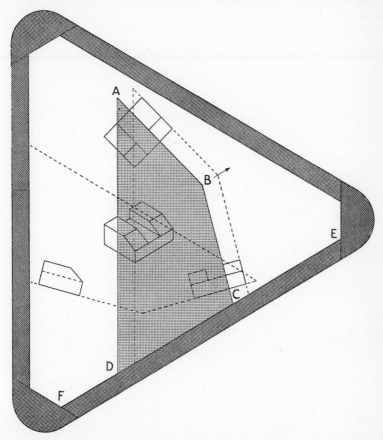

Fig. 87. The triangular framework and quadrangle used in Shick's 'United Projection', which relates directly all points in the orthographic outlines and in the central isometric view.

obliged to fit every type of pictorial drawing to the principle of projection that formal oblique projection appeared. It was postulated that such a view or picture was obtained theoretically by projecting an object by parallel projectors on to a plane parallel to one of the object's faces, the projectors being obliquely inclined to the projection plane. In other words a primary geometry was invented to account for a secondary geometry which had been in use for ages. True as this projectional relationship is, it has never yet proved to be of any use. An oblique view of an object can be drawn without any idea of the nature of projection – and even if its form is explained in terms of projection, one will still continue to draw it in the same way.

18

Technical Illustration

ENGINEERING as a whole and engineering drawing have progressed together. Through modern engineering drawing methods, engineering has been able to develop to its present state of complexity. From the simple machines which were depicted on one sheet of paper, we can now design and build extremely large and complex projects, such as atomic power stations and supersonic aircraft, using a series of drawings – running into thousands, or even tens and hundreds of thousands – which define everything from the overall plan down to the smallest detail. Through modern engineering drawings, the manufacture or construction of equipment or plant can be broken down and contracted, sub-contracted and sub-sub-contracted out in a complexity of organisation far beyond Redtenbacher's wildest dreams. Nobody sees in total at one time all the drawings which are used in the design of a large project, but the organisation which allows a design to progress and which makes and processes all these drawings is one of the wonders of our age.

The profusion of these engineering drawings, which are often covered with dimensions and notes concerning tolerances, finishes, testing methods, part lists and so on, makes it extremely difficult to explain to an outsider – that is, one not directly involved in the design or manufacture of a product – its essential nature. Busy executives, salesmen, maintenance men and so on, cannot spend hours trying to unravel a multitude of drawings to find one piece of information essential to them. Growing up rapidly beside technical engineering drawing is the activity known as technical illustration. Whilst a set of engineering drawings are on their way to the workshops to control manufacture, another set will often be on their way to the publications department, which has to reinterpret these drawings for the production of instruction and maintenance manuals and even for advertising. The criteria are quite different; whereas the technical engineering drawings have to define the parts of a piece of equipment so that they can be manufactured successfully, the technical illustrations will be used by persons who only have to assemble or dismantle existing parts, or who will only need to know how something works.

This takes us right back to the differences between the drawing philosophies of Monge and Farish – descriptive geometry to define parts, and isometrical perspective to demonstrate arrangements for assembly. Indeed, a generation ago when technical illustration was a side function of the engineering drawing office, isometric projection was often used. Technical illustration, however, goes back much further than this to the technical drawings of the Middle Ages which were pictorial in form and which were only intended to convey the general idea of some arrangement of elements. There are many illustrations from this period which are not just pictures in the ordinary sense, but true technical illustrations, in that they show imaginary conditions with parts cut away or dismantled for identification. By far the most interesting of this age are those of Agricola's *De re metallica* and an example is shown in Fig. 88.

This demonstrates an endless chain drive with buckets for lifting water out of a mine – incidentally, one of the driving forces behind mechanical invention, including that of the steam engine, which heralded the Industrial Revolution – the chain being driven by hand through reduction gearing. All this gear was, in fact, underground, and the artist has 'cut-away' the earth where necessary to expose the relevant parts. The array of dismantled parts in the foreground is a repetition of the parts in the mechanism 'exploded', or shown individually, for identification purposes – a sort of graphic parts list. The man is demonstrating how the buckets and chain are assembled. An earlier book *De la pirotechnia*, by Vannoccio Biringuccio had a few interesting drawings of this nature, but they were not so detailed as the famous Agricola drawings. The latter are, indeed, a unique record of their time which cannot fail to be of absorbing interest to all engineers, draughtsmen and illustrators. There are 289 of these illustrations, but they were made by professional engravers and not by Agricola himself.

Many persons in the late Middle Ages contrived to draw up works containing a record of contemporary practice, and some of the most interesting of these are the note-books of Leonardo da Vinci. He left a number of these on painting, on the flight of birds,

---

Fig. 88. A chain and dipper pump as illustrated in Georgius Agricola's *De re metallica* of 1556. This displays a 'cut-away' technique to show the parts of the gear underground, and the 'exploding' technique to show the various parts which go to make up the assembly.

on hydraulics, on anatomy, on mechanics and machines and so on. They are justly famous because, instead of being just records of what was generally known or was contemporary practice, they also included da Vinci's own, and mainly new, ideas. From the engineer's point of view, his books on machines are of the most interest, but this interest lies mostly in his progressive mechanical ideas and his grasp of the elements of mechanism, which he assembled in all manner of ways. The drawings themselves are not of a consistent standard, however, ranging from beautiful perspective sketches to the roughest of elementary outlines and, whilst from the designer's point of view they are well worth study, da Vinci's works and drawings made little contribution to technical drawing theory or practice. His drawings are mentioned under this section because the forms they take are more reminiscent of technical illustration than engineering drawing; although in truth many of them are really inventive sketching or thinking on paper. Some of the da Vinci drawings of machines are descriptions of general practice of the time; some are of his own inventions or design modifications, many of which were actually put into effect by him; and yet others are just ideas often far in advance of what contemporary technology could accomplish. At one time it was thought that Leonardo's ideas had little effect on subsequent history because many of the manuscripts were not published until modern times; however, it has been established that, although unpublished, these works were lent to others and had some circulation both during and after da Vinci's lifetime, greatly affecting the thinking of others.

One of Leonardo's drawings of machines is shown in Fig. 89. It is from the *Codex Atlanticus*, a manuscript of 403 sheets, now in the Biblioteca Ambrosiana, Milan. It came back to Italy from Spain about 1604, but was taken to France in 1796 as the result of Napoleon's campaign in Italy. It was to help superintend the collection and dispatch of Italian works of art, valued manuscripts, etc., that Gaspard Monge was ordered to leave the École Polytechnique in its early days. Possibly he was personally responsible for the *Codex's* journey to France. However, it was restored to Italy in 1815.

Fig. 89 is not one reproduced very often, for mechanically it is rather ambiguous. It has, all the same, considerable interest value in our present context, in that it foreshadows modern technical illustration technique. To the left is the machine assembled; to the right, its parts are 'exploded', not haphazardly as in Agricola's illustrations, but along natural axes of assembly. Notice the clever conservation of space achieved by overlapping the various parts, although no part is covered by another to an extent which would cause ambiguity of interpretation. This is preferable to parts exploded to the extent where each is shown in isolation, for the whole 'hangs together' better. Whilst da Vinci probably drew thus instinctively, modern analysis of the psychology of seeing has led to such practices becoming a recognised part of the philosophy of technical illustration today.

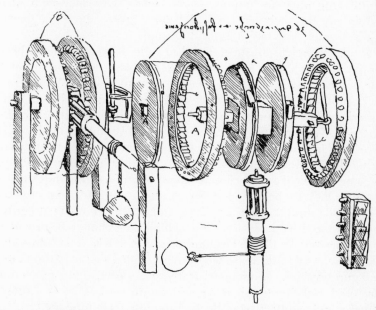

Fig. 89. A sketch from Leonardo da Vinci's *Codex Atlanticus* showing an 'exploded view' of a weight-driven motor. The operation of the motor is obscure, but the drawing technique is notable.

Drawings of the 'instructive' type continued to appear throughout the centuries getting progressively 'cleaner'. Diderot's *Encyclopedia* of the 18th century contains a vast assembly of such illustrations which, again, have become a unique legacy to us of life in those times. The 'cleanness' was due partly to artists with more advanced techniques and concepts, and partly to the change from woodcuts to metal engravings which allowed of very fine line-work.

The art of technical illustration declined noticeably around the beginning of the 19th century. The form of machines and the shapes of their individual parts were becoming much more complex than hitherto and, in order that the machines themselves should materialise at all, considerable numbers of engineering drawings, in the form of plans and elevations, were necessary. When, in the increasing number of books and encyclopedias, these machines were described and illustrations were required, the engravers merely copied the original plans in so far as they considered them relevant, embellishing these 'pictures' with shading in the form of hatching. The dividing engines of Ramsden, Babbage's calculating engines, pin-making machines, pumps, machine tools and so on were treated in this way and these records have been of great value to engineering historians. Fig. 65 is a typical example.

Whilst technical illustration did not die, it seems to have been temporarily eclipsed. Modern technical illustration, like so much else in the drawing field, was developed by and for the Armed Services, notably the Royal Navy and the Royal Air Force. The American Armed Forces have also played a similar part, especially in the last generation. The impetus probably started in the First World War when on the one hand large numbers of persons were being drafted into service whilst on the other hand war began to become technical and backed by a vast manufacturing industry.

Guns had to be stripped for examination and correctly reassembled; aircraft, engines, ships and other complicated equipment had to be kept serviceable and handbooks had to be provided so that persons could quickly familiarise themselves. The Admiralty soon developed a 'standard' pattern for exploding the parts of guns and gun breeches. Axonometric rather than perspective projection was used and the drawings were in simple outline using a three-dimensional counterpart of the line-shading technique used earlier on engineers' drawings. The technique used is illustrated in Fig. 90.

There are, of course, many kinds of technical illustrations besides exploded views for assembly purposes, and over time these were all absorbed by industry until, today, it is rare to find a large engineering company without a special illustration section. Within these firms there have been many experiments in techniques such as the imparting of three-dimensional effects by various types of shading and so on, but it is worth noting that there is a tendency to dispense with the frills and go back to the simple outline type of illustration. There are many reasons for this. To begin with there is quite a parallel between technical illustration and engineering drawing where the Armed Services are concerned. The Services are one of industry's largest customers, and just as they laid down how their engineering drawings should be made, so they have stated clearly what sort of illustrations they want in manuals to accompany equipment. To save overheads there is naturally a tendency for a firm to make all its illustrations to one standard. Secondly, the expense of most things today rests in the cost of labour, and any acceptable method which is light on labour is welcome.

There is also, possibly, a more subtle reason for the reversion to simple line illustrations, in that the technique of illustration and the handling of line-work is much better understood than it was.

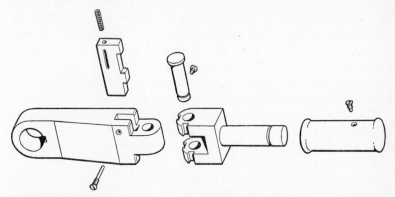

Fig. 90. Illustrating the standard method for 'exploded' views adopted by the Admiralty for instruction handbooks in the 1930s. Similar standard methods are coming back into industry for they allow any number of widely dispersed illustrators to produce work which will match up to form a uniform whole. The simple line-work and standard shadow techniques will reproduce by any method from duplication to photogravure printing. Varying the line thicknesses is similar to the shadow lining used on 19th-century orthographic drawings.

This is reflected quite well in text-books. Until recently, the text-books that were available gave the impression that technical illustration was the knowledge of how to draw 'rigorous' shapes in perspective and axonometric projections, supplemented later by suggested methods of shading drawings. It took a long time to recognise that technical illustration was much more than this; that it was a medium for imparting information, and that it was based upon a sound knowledge of visual communication, that is, the psychology of seeing as distinct from the principles of projection. Through the relative positioning of parts and the variation of line thicknesses, this approach allows a line drawing such as Fig. 90 to be interpreted, sometimes, more easily than an artistic presentation in tone.

Modern technical illustration as a widespread activity in the hands of professionals is quite young, and for this reason insufficient time has elapsed to be able to discern any clear trends. In America the interpretation is, perhaps, wider under the heading of 'engineering illustration', and it is concerned with practically all forms of drawing used for communication apart from those directly within the province of design and manufacture. The beginnings of this movement probably go back to the war years, when one of the most remarkable experiments in using perspective drawings was carried out in the works of the Douglas Aircraft Company by a group of draughtsmen and production engineers under the direction of George Tharrett, whose book, *Aircraft Production Illustration** describing the techniques, became well known. It was, he said, '. . . a device or method for speeding the production of mechanical assemblies. These illustrations break down and depict in simple, easily-understood drawings the operations necessary to manufacture and assemble each component part of an assembly.'

This was a more ambitious attempt at what was briefly mentioned in the previous chapter – the use of axonometric drawings to supplement standard orthographic views. It used perspective as a basis and was more ambitious because it was not just an attempt to illustrate the shape of objects to aid production; instead it was an approach by persons who really saw the possibilities in using visual communication to depict operations on or with things, rather than just the things themselves. Whilst the situation is still fluid, one has the impression that illustration is used internally in many American companies as much as externally.

Technical illustration in Britain has little, if any, connection with production illustration, partly because the latter never really got a foothold in industry. As a result, illustration is mainly concerned with handbooks, leaflets and advertising media for external use. The tendency is for illustration to become just a section of the Publications Department with visual matters often under the direction of a technical writer trained in verbal communication. Such situations often right themselves in time as understanding and abilities broaden, but whereas in the u.s.a. there is a Society of Engineering Illustrators, in Britain the fraternity is split between the Society of Industrial Artists and the newly formed Society of Technical Authors and Illustrators.

* Ref. 72. A short review of this system with illustrations is given in Ref. 58.

19

Today and Tomorrow

It is difficult and possibly unwise to speculate too much about future trends, and to do this at all it is necessary to consider engineering drawing in all its different aspects separately.

Sketching, or getting ideas onto paper in some form or other, will presumably always be with us. Such drawings range through various stages of abstraction down to the near concrete – they can take the form of symbols as in the case of circuit and flow diagrams, or be more formal pictures where the shapes of actual parts, or machines as a whole, are concerned. There is, indeed, considerable scope for the improvement of general sketching practice as a means of 'thinking' on paper or as an aid to the imagination.

Design has been said to be the process of taking a vague, imagined solution to an engineering problem and giving it more and more certainty through making drawings, calculations and tests. After sketching, the next step to certainty is the making of scaled layout drawings, which invariably show up problems not apparent in sketches. The practice of making 'ideal representations' on paper will undoubtedly continue, although in certain industries, where design is largely a matter of arranging existing equipment, there is a trend towards the use of models.

The chemical and oil industries have pioneered this model method and it is being taken up by many concerned with factory layout, where plastic models of machines, etc. are used, and in pipework where the draughtsman works with wire and soldering iron, building up from flow sheets a model of the projected design. These models are often used instead of drawings by both the constructors and maintenance staff, and modifications are made on them as well as on the actual equipment. Some drawings, naturally, have to be made and these are usually horizontal and vertical sections, as considered necessary, upon which the true positions of pipe centres are recorded. In complex areas a draughtsman produces isometric sketches to show which pipe goes over or under which. These models allow pipe runs to be in the optimum positions. With normal three-view drawings the three-dimensional pipe runs are difficult to visualise, with the result that pipes are invariably 'right-routed' or 'square-routed', that is drawn, and so made, parallel or at right angles to the three principal planes. With models there is no difficulty in running pipes from point to point by the shortest practicable routes, no matter at what angles they run.

Since models like this are expensive to construct—remember that they are not built from drawings, but are straight three-dimensional creations—it would be even more costly if they had to be measured up and recorded additionally in the form of drawings. However, records of a complicated refinery layout sometimes need to be kept at a number of places and, to overcome the expense of making drawings, a new method based upon photography is increasingly used.

The camera may be considered as a 'mechanical' drawing machine which will automatically make perspective pictures (using the original primary geometry—see Chapter 1). For engineering purposes true shape views are generally required, however, and the successful use of photography has depended upon a method of deducing plans and elevations from perspective photographs. This science is known as photogrammetry, although today it has rather a different meaning in practice from the original concept. Photogrammetry in principle is nearly as old as perspective itself. We saw in the chapter on perspective that Leonardo da Vinci showed how to deduce true information from a perspective drawing *given certain information*. Given just a photograph one can deduce nothing, although one can if one knows the true centre of vision (the print might be only a section of a photograph taken), the focal length of the camera and the enlargement of the print. Alternatively, one can work perspective backwards if one knows some of the dimensions of the object photographed, or the ratio of certain dimensions. Even so, any errors in this given information will give magnified errors in the true information extracted.

Modern methods of photogrammetry are based on stereoscopic principles developed from air photography practice. Most readers will have viewed stereoscopic pictures through a special viewer which contains two lenses and spaces for the two photographs. These photographs—which may be in colour—are taken with two cameras, one viewing what the left eye would see and one what the right eye would see. Through the viewer one thus has a reconstruction of what would be seen if the actual object or scene were there. The modern practice with pipework layout models is to photograph them from appropriate directions stereoscopically. These photographs are then filed. If at a later date drawings of some particular section are required and the model is not available, the relevant twin photographs are placed in a 'Stereo-autographic'* instrument and the operator produces front and side views (projections) by, in effect, tracing over the 'three-dimensional' object with a 'three-dimensional' pointer—a black spot seen through the eyepieces, which can be made to move vertically and horizontally and 'into' the picture stereoscopically.

With pipe runs and similar layout jobs models are appropriate because wire, representing pipes, is easy to handle and shape. However, the use of models is limited in design, for in most engineering the parts required are of special shapes or characters and are non-existent. On the whole there is yet no substitute for drawing in design work and there may well never be.

As the design proceeds drawings are used to record and communicate shapes (and other attributes) of detail parts. It is probably in this field that most changes are likely to take place. Now that engineering techniques are spreading into industrial design, furniture manufacture, the production of household goods and so on—even cups, buckets and barrels are today mass-produced on machines in plastics—the number of drawings made and handled is becoming prodigious. For storing and handling there is a trend towards the use of micro-film which offers many advantages. Very large reductions in size are made with the micro-filming of engineering drawings and this has to be taken increasingly into account by those concerned with symbols and drawing standardisation generally. (Fig. 63 was reproduced from the original by microfilm.)

National drawing standards in any case only deal with that part of engineering drawing practice which can be considered common to all industry. Superimposed upon this are innumerable practices used by specific industries or by individual firms to fit particular circumstances. For instance, in aircraft manufacture, where there is still a great deal of sheet metal work, drawings are often printed straight down on to the metal sheet, sometimes from original master drawings, sometimes from photo-copies. All sorts of symbols are used on these drawings to represent holes of different sizes and finishes, and sometimes even to represent the type of rivets or screws to be used. This technique is an extension of the lofting practice mentioned in the chapter on ship draughting and is the modern

* Leland Instruments, London; Officine Galileo, Italy.

counterpart of the marking out of wood and stone by the carpenters and stone-cutters.

Probably no single person has a really complete picture of the varied and many complex drawing practices in existence throughout industry, and it is the complexity of this situation which makes it difficult to get national standards adopted throughout industry.

New drawing techniques tend to supplement old ones rather than to replace them completely, so that the total vocabulary of engineering drawing continues to increase. If one looks about industry today closely, from the mighty industrial combines to the humble odd jobbing shops, one can see the history of a hundred years of engineering existing simultaneously, and one can find drawings which cover this range. In prototype work it is still not uncommon to find craftsmen building a machine from a general arrangement drawing without special drawings of details, just as was the normal practice a hundred years ago. Sometimes when a special 'one-off' job is broken down in drawings of details, one can still see basic sizes quoted with notes on the type of fit required. Occasionally a rough sketch is still given to a craftsman for some odd, non-critical job.

This 'spread' of drawing methods is worth keeping in mind, for today new equipment is introducing yet newer types of drawings, these becoming for the time being new additions rather than replacements. One such new type of drawing is that made for the production of parts on electronically controlled machine tools, such as the example in Fig. 91.

The item depicted is a special cam-plate and the drawing is a function of the actual method of machining. The cutter is positioned at any instant by reference to three co-ordinate values. All the outlines – curves or straight lines – are generated by a constant stream of signals giving successive positions for the cutter in terms of co-ordinate values. The basic co-ordinates are given in the table accompanying the outlines; all the intermediate points' positions are interpolated by the machine. The circular arcs are not cut as on a lathe by physically generating an arc, but are produced by the combined motion of the cutter in the X and Y directions according to the general equation $R^2 = X^2 + Y^2$. Straight lines are produced between two given points according to the general equation $Y = MX + N$.

We are back, indeed, to Descartes's and to Monge's original method of defining the position of a point in space by virtue of its distances from three given reference planes. In a sense, the electronic apparatus defines one by one the points on the surface of the cam and the cutter moves accordingly from point to point. It is true that in this case the cam is basically two-dimensional and that, except for one or two adjustments of cutter height, the cutter traces paths in the X and Y plane only. However, we have to recognise that

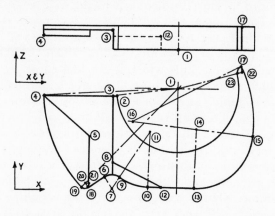

CO-ORD POINT	X	Y	Z	RADIUS
1	0	0	1·2500	4·5620 2·0624
2	θ2·0472	θ ·2500	2·0000	2·0626
3	θ2·1874	θ ·2500	1·8750	
4	θ4·5556	θ ·2500	1·6880	
5	θ2·9688	θ1·5814	2·0000	
6	θ2·5126	θ2·8402	2·0000	
20	θ3·1330	θ3·0866	2·0000	·1644
21	θ2·9688	θ3·0866	2·0000	
22	2·1776	·5676	2·0000	·1876
23	1·9950	·5220	2·0000	

Fig. 91. A drawing of a component dimensioned for machining on an electronically-controlled machine tool.

this complicated apparatus may well be only a crude form of the 'machining' practice of the future–where, incidentally, material might be removed chemically or electrically instead of by cutting forces which cause distortion and thus inaccuracy.

Strictly speaking most metal forming operations today are crude, although we do not like to think of them in that way. The whole system of tolerancing and specification of shape variations on drawings is an admission of this crudity. Even the process of inspecting, the checking of dimensions and forms after a part is manufactured, is an admission of this crudity, although we have come to accept it as the norm.

Looked at ideally, the whole pattern of today's production is a sort of interim measure – although it might well be with us for a long time. The ultimate aim will be to produce parts which are as near to the ideal abstractions as to make no practical difference. We may eventually look forward to a time when any one part can be produced on a machine which is not limited to certain single functions such as turning, drilling, slotting, etc., but which will be capable of machining any shape at one setting according to the instructions given. These instructions will be as in Fig. 91 – the true dimensions, the true centres, etc. Since this hypothetical machine will cut everything true within its inherent accuracy, say plus or minus one ten-thousandth of an inch, there will be no need to specify tolerances, geometrical or otherwise, for these will be meaningless to the machine. Neither will dimensional inspection be necessary, for the machine will work very much more accurately than any person and will be continually checking every point as it forms it on the part's surface.

This is, possibly, looking rather a long way ahead, but it allows us to see drawings such as Fig. 91 in better perspective. Although this is at present a special type of drawing, it specifies the true ideal, and it leads us to the conclusion that, in time, it may be quite sufficient for a designer to specify the true ideal and leave it at that. It is interesting to note that the true ideal is specified by actual figures for co-ordinate points and not by the outline of the drawing, for this cannot possibly display the true shape required of the product; for consider, apart from the draughtsman's inherent inaccuracy, if the paper distorts or stretches this cannot possibly mean that the part must be machined distorted or larger.

Another very interesting field of speculation is opened up by Fig. 92. This drawing was produced in less than a quarter of a second via a computer-controlled cathode-ray tube. This, naturally, makes one wonder – is there anything computers cannot do? Wonderful as this is, the simple statement that it was drawn by a computer is rather misleading as will be seen by considering the nature of computers and the nature of drawings.

Both of these are worth considering here for two reasons. Firstly, computers are going to play an increasingly important part in our lives. Secondly, one might think that a book like this is making rather heavy going of such a 'simple' subject as drawing. The complexity of drawing is shown up very clearly when we try to see what would be required of a computer to handle drawings, and this makes a fitting topic with which to close this book.

The rapid development of computers has been most marked in their continual increase in speed of operation. Today, it is quite normal to hear of a computer working at the rate of hundreds of

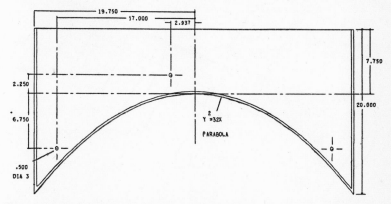

Fig. 92. A parabolic template drawn on the 'Charactron' Shaped-Beam Tube and subsequently photographed onto microfilm.

thousands of operations a second. To keep pace with computing speeds a number of devices have been invented to record computer outputs at high speed. One of these resulted from the combining of the cathode-ray tube with the magic lantern in the form of a 'Charactron' Shaped-Beam Tube. As in more conventional tubes, a beam of electrons is generated in an electron gun, accelerated and introduced into a field between co-planar electrostatic plates. A special element (see Fig. 93) called the 'matrix' is located at a precise distance beyond the deflection plates. This matrix is a thin metal disc centred on the electron gun axis at right angles to the beam. Generally sixty-four minute characters in an eight by eight array are precision-etched through the matrix disc. Varying the voltage of the plates as required deflects the beam so that electrons are 'fired' through any one of the sixty-four matrix stencils. The beam, which now has the sections of the stencil through which it passed, is then centred and finally again deflected by voltages to any desired position on the tube screen. In this way up to 20,000 characters a second can be 'drawn' on the tube screen as the computer directs. Of course, these drawn characters only have a transient existence and they are therefore photographed by a special camera. The lettering on Figs. 92 and 94 was produced in this way, that is, drawn by electrons, and this may be compared with the lettering in Fig. 93 which is printed by conventional means.

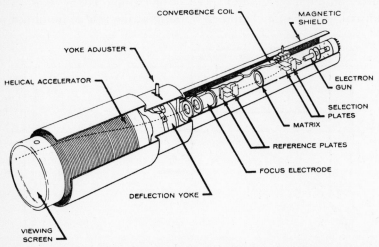

Fig. 93. The 'Charactron' Shaped-Beam Tube. Developed initially to display characters as instructed by computer at rates of up to 20,000 characters per second, it has recently been used experimentally to make drawings from computer information.

The tube can, of course, also produce a spot of light, and if this spot is moved over the tube face it effectively 'draws', a permanent 'picture' being captured on the photographic plate. The designers of this equipment therefore added two further units to their equipment—an axis generator and a vector generator. The former draws horizontal and vertical axes starting at any specified point in the display area, while the latter draws straight lines between any two given points regardless of angle.

The practical application of this equipment, so far as engineering drawing is concerned—it has other scientific uses—is as yet confined to a very small field. In Fig. 91 we saw a drawing with tabulations for use with a computer-controlled machine tool. The tabulations, in this case, have to be typed out on a machine which produces punched tape; the holes formed in the tape are fed into the computer, which then issues instructions to the machine tool either in

228

the form of voltage variations or in pulse signals. The trouble is that before the part can be machined, the tape has to be checked in case someone has punched the wrong holes in it in error. This can, of course, be checked against the tabulated figures, though this is tedious; what, however, if some of these are wrong? Really the tape needs to be checked against the drawing, and this has been done by feeding the tape into a computer which draws upon the tube face the shape recorded. This drawing and the original should tally. Small errors cannot, of course, be detected, but any blatant errors will show up.

The object depicted in Fig. 92 is a template cut from a piece of plate and it is, therefore, really a two-dimensional shape. What appears to be very much more interesting is Fig. 94, which shows two views of a strange looking rectilineal shape which was drawn by way of the 'Charactron' beam tube in half a second. It is, as marked, only a feasibility study, but it is worth examining.

When this feasibility study was first publicised it gave the impression that a computer was at hand which could draw in the same sense as the draughtsman. This was occasioned by the two related views. If only one view had been given it would have been just a flat pattern of lines. The two views, however, suggest that a three-dimensional shape is being handled by a computer. Indeed, one draughtsman wrote to the technical press pointing out that the computer had omitted one line. Of course, the computer had done no such thing, since it had no idea what it was 'drawing'. It simply took the instructions given to it –in the form of the co-ordinates of the end points of lines–interpolated the points in between, and traced the required lines. The co-ordinate points were put in by the programmer punching them on to a tape, and he in turn got them from an original drawing of the shapes. Naturally, if he omitted a line so would this 'drawing apparatus'.

The cathode-ray tube and the computer were, in effect, the 'pencil', the 'hand' and the 'rule'–the brain which controlled them and thought in three-dimensions was outside this arrangement, in the person of the draughtsman who made the original drawing. If an electronic brain were, then, produced which could 'think' in terms of three-dimensional shapes, or even two-dimensional shapes, the beam tube and associated apparatus would be suitable equipment for recording its output.

It is very unlikely that any such machine can be made–at least, economically–in the foreseeable future. The trouble is that

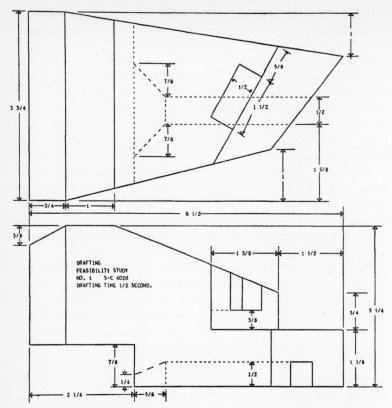

Fig. 94. Drafting Feasibility Study No. 1. Drawn in half a second from a programme fed to a computer.

computers have no senses that can make them aware of the world as we know it – particularly visually. On the other hand, we do not, and probably cannot, conceive shapes in terms of algebraical expressions or co-ordinate points. Our knowledge of shape is bound up with our visual sense and experience, and our first attempt at pinning down any shape we think of is to draw it, that is make a visual representation. Since we have already then drawn it there is no point in using a computer to draw it for us, especially as we should have to convert our drawing into another language suitable for a computer to handle.

Whilst we may not, therefore, expect computers to take the place of draughtsmen, there are nevertheless some special cases where computers can be used with advantage. They might, for instance, be useful for drawing cam profiles, since all the basic data —minimum radius, lift(s), periods of dwell, etc.—can be given in terms of numbers. They might also be useful for drawing mathematically defined profiles such as aero-foils, propeller- and turbine-blade sections, which otherwise would entail the tedious plotting of points.

These are, however, exceptions, and it seems likely that pencils and paper—and more particularly the ability to use them in the many diverse techniques of drawing—will be with us for a long, long time.

BIBLIOGRAPHY

Works are listed alphabetically under author's name. The numbers correspond to those given in the text at the end of quotations, etc.

1 Abbott, W.: *The Theory and Practice of Perspective*, Blackie, London, 1950.

2 Agricola, Georgius: *De re metallica* (1556), English translation by H. C. & L. H. Hoover, London, 1912.

3 Alberti, Leone Battista: *De re aedificatoria* (1435), English translation by J. Leoni, London, 1755.

4 Armengaud, J. E., Armengaud, G. E., & Amouroux: *The Practical Draughtsman's Book of Industrial Design, forming a Complete Course of Mechanical Engineering and Architectural Drawing*, rewritten by W. Johnson, London, 1853.

5 Bicknell, C.: *Guide to the Prehistoric Rock Engravings in the Italian Maritime Alps*, 1913.

6 Binns, W.: *Elementary Treatise on Orthographic Projection, being a New Method of Teaching the Science of Mechanical and Engineering Drawing*, London, 1857.

7 Blagrave, John: *The Mathematical Jewel*, London, 1582.

8 Blagrave, John: *Astrolabium Uranicum Generale*, London, 1596.

9 Blagrave, John: *The Art of Dyalling in Two Parts, shewing how to make dyals to all plaines*, etc., London, 1609.

10 Booker, P. J.: *Direct Pictorial Projection*, Engineering Drawing & Design, London, Vol. 3, No. 4, 1949, Nos. 1 & 2, Vol. 4, 1950.

11 Bosse, Abraham: *La Manière universelle de M. Desargues pour poser l'essieu, etc. aux cadrans au soleil*, Paris, 1643.

12 Bosse, Abraham: *Mr. Desargues Universal Way of Dyalling*, translation of above by Daniel King, London, 1659.

13 Bosse, Abraham: *La Pratique du trait à preuves de M. Desargues Lyonnois, pour la coupe des pierres en l'architecture*, Paris, 1663.

14 Bradley, Thomas: *Practical Geometry*, Society for Diffusion of Useful Knowledge, London, 1836.

15 Clegg, S., Junr.: *Architecture of Machinery, an Essay on Propriety of Form and Proportion*, London, 1852.

16 Commandine: *Ptolemoei Planisphaerium*, Venice, 1558.

17 Commandine: *Ptolemoei de Analemmate*, Rome, 1562.

18 Cunningham, A. W.: *Notes on the History, Methods and Technological Importance of Descriptive Geometry*, Edinburgh, 1868.

19 Davidson, Ellis A.: *Linear Drawing*, London, 1868.

20 Davidson, Ellis A.: *Projection*, London, 1868.

21 Davidson, Ellis A.: *Practical Perspective*, London, 1870.

22 Davidson, Ellis A.: *Drawing for Machinists and Engineers*, London, *c.* 1870.

Desargues, Gérard: see Bosse, Abraham.

23 Descartes, René: *Discours de la méthode*, 1637.

24 Descartes, René: *The Geometry of René Descartes*, translation of 'Geometrical Matters' from above by D. E. S. & M. L. Latham, with French facsimile, Dover, New York, 1954.

25 Diderot, Denis, and d'Alembert, J. L.: *Encyclopédie ou Dictionnaire raisonné des sciences, des arts et des métiers*, 35 Volumes, Paris, 1751–1780.

26 Diderot, Denis: *A Diderot Pictorial Encyclopedia of Trades and Industry*, Edited by C. C. Gillispie, Dover, New York, 1959.

27 Duerer, Albrecht: *Unterweysung der Messung*, 1525.

28 Duerer, Albrecht: *Hierinn sind begriffen vier Bücher von menschlicher Proportion. . .* , Nuremberg, 1528.

29 Dupin, Françoise, Pierre, Charles: *Essai historique sur les services et les travaux scientifiques de Gaspard Monge*, Paris, 1819.

30 Dupin, Françoise, Pierre, Charles: *Développements de géométrie avec des applications à la stabilité des vaisseaux*, Paris, 1813.

Dürer, see Duerer.

31 Eckhart, L.: *Ein neues Schrägrissverfahren*, V.D.I. Zeitschrift, No. 15, 9 April, 1938.

32 Farish, William: *On Isometrical Perspective*, Cambridge Philosophical Society Transactions, Vol. 1, pp. 1-20, 1822.

33 Feldhaus, Franz Maria: *Geschichte des technischen Zeichnens*, Wilhelmshaven, 1953.

34 Hachette, J. N. P.: *Traité élémentaire des machines*, 4th Ed., Paris, 1811.

35 Hachette, J. N. P.: *Applications de géométrie descriptive*, Paris, 1817.

36 Harrison, J., & Baxandall, G. A: *Practical Plane and Solid Geometry*, Macmillan, London, 1901.

37 Healy, W. L., & Rau, A. H.: *Simplified Drafting Practice*, Wiley, New York, 1953.

38 Heather, J. F.: *An Elementary Treatise on Descriptive Geometry with a Theory of Shadows and of Perspective, extracted from the French of Gaspard Monge, to which is added a Description of the Principles and Practice of Isometrical Projection*, London, 1851.

39 Higbee, Frederic G.: *The Development of Graphical Representation*, Journal of Engineering Drawing, May, 1958. Given at Engineering Drawing Division of A.S.E.E. Summer School, 1946. Proceedings published McGraw-Hill Book Co.

40 Hilken, T. J. N.: *The Ingenious Mr. Farish*, Cambridge Review, Vol. LXXXI, No. 1974, Feb. 20, 1960.

41 Hoelscher, Randolph P, & Springer, Clifford C.: *Engineering Drawing and Geometry*, Wiley, New York, 1956, 1961.

42 Klemm, Friedrich: *A History of Western Technology*, Allen & Unwin, London, 1959, translation of 'Technik: eine Geschichte ihrer

BIBLIOGRAPHY

Probleme', Verlag Karl Alber, 1954.

43 Launay, L. de: *Monge, fondateur de l'École Polytechnique*, Paris, 1933.

44 Leroy, C. F. A.: *Traité de géométrie descriptive, suivie de la méthode des plans côtés*, 2 Vols., Paris, 1867.

45 Low, David Allan: *Practical Geometry and Graphics*, Longmans Green, London, 1912

46 Low, David Allan: *An Introduction to Machine Drawing and Design*, Longmans Green, London, 1914.

47 Marolois, Samuel: *La Perspective contenant tant la théorie que la practique et instruction fondamentale d'icelle, etc.*, Amsterdam, 1629.

48 McGuire, J. G.: *Dimensioning and Shop Processes*, Texas Engineering Experiment Station, USA, Bulletin No. 88, 1945.

49 McGuire, J. G.: *A New Approach to Axonometric Projection and its Application to Shop Drawings*, Texas Engineering Experiment Station, USA, Bulletin No. 79, 1944.

50 McGuire, J. G., Barton, R. L., & Mason, P. M.: *Basic Models for Technical Drawing*, Texas Engineering Experiment Station, USA, Bulletin No. 115, 1949.

51 Monge, Gaspard: *Géométrie descriptive*, Paris, 1795, etc.

52 Monge, Gaspard: *Géométrie descriptive, suivie d'une théorie des ombres et de la perspective, extraite des papiers de l'auteur par M. Brisson*, Paris, 7th Ed., 1847.

53 Muller, J.: *Practical Fortification*, London, 1755.

54 Noble, George: *Drawing*, Dominion Engineer, Dominion Engineering Co. Ltd., Montreal, Canada, Vol. 23, No. 4, 1956.

55 Noble, George: *A New Canadian Drawing Standard*, Dominion Engineer, Dominion Engineering Co. Ltd., Montreal, Canada, Vol. 26, No. 4, 1959.

56 Noizet, François Joseph: *Principes de fortification*, 2 Vols., Paris, 1859.

57 Noizet, Saint Paul: *Traité complet de fortification*, 2 Vols., Paris, 1799, 1800.

58 Parkinson, A. C.: *Pictorial Drawing for Engineers*, Pitman, London, 1953.

59 Redtenbacher, Ferdinand: *Prinzipien der Mechanik und des Maschinenbaues*, Mannheim, 1852.

60 Robinet: *Cours complet de dessin des machines*, Hachette, Paris, 1842.

61 Roe, Joseph W.: *Interchangeable Manufacture*, Transactions of Newcomen Society, Vol. 17, pp. 165-174, 1936-37.

62 Rose, Joshua: *Mechanical Drawing Self-Taught*, Philadelphia, 1883, 1900.

63 Sawyer, D. D.: *Education by Drawing*, Cambridge University Press, 1943.

64 Schmid, Theodor: *Darstellende Geometrie, Vol. 1, Orthogonale Axonometrie*, Vienna, 1922.

65 Schuessler, Rudolf: *Orthogonale Axonometrie, ein Lehrbuch zum Selbststudium*, Leipzig & Berlin, 1905.

BIBLIOGRAPHY

66 Shick, Wayne L.: *Axonometric Projection: New Concepts and Drawing Instruments*, University of Illinois, 9 April, 1959.

67 Sterland, E. G.: *The Early History of the Teaching of Engineering in Cambridge*, Transactions of Newcomen Society, Vol. 28, pp. 263-75, 1951-53.

68 Sutherland, William: *The Shipbuilders Assistant, or some Essays towards Compleating the Art of Marine Architecture*, London, 1711.

69 Svensen, Carl Lars: *Essentials of Drafting*, Van Nostrand, New York, 1918, 1923, 1943.

70 Taton, René: *L'Œuvre scientifique de Monge*, Paris, 1951.

71 Taton, René: *L'Histoire de la géométrie descriptive*, Paris, 1954.

72 Tharratt, George: *Aircraft Production Illustration*, McGraw-Hill, New York, 1946.

73 Vasari, Giorgio: *The Lives of the Painters, Sculptors and Architects*, Italy, 1551.

74 Vitruvius: *The Ten Books on Architecture*, translated by M. H. Morgan, Harvard University Press, 1914; Dover, New York, 1960.

75 Walters, W. E.: *Three-Dimensional Engineering Drawing*, Pen-in-Hand, Oxford, 1949.

76 Wellman, B. Leighton: *What is Fundamental in Descriptive Geometry?*, A.S.E.E. Engineering Drawing Division Annual Meeting, 1949.

77 *ABC Conference on Unification of Engineering Practice, Toronto, Oct. 1957*, Canadian Standards Association, 1958.

78 *American Standard Drawing and Drafting Room Practice*, ASA Z14.1, American Standards Association, 1935, etc.

79 *American Drafting Standards Manual*, American Society of Mechanical Engineers (being published in Sections; 11 Sections available in 1961).

80 *Biographie universelle, ancienne et moderne, Vol. 29*, Paris, 1821. (Contains a short biography of Monge.)

81 *Dimensional Analysis of Engineering Designs, Vol. 1, Components*, H.M.S.O., London, 1948.

82 *Engineering Drawing Office Practice*, British Engineering Standards Association (now B.S.I.), Standard N. 308, 1927.

83 *Engineering Drawing Office Practice*, B.S.I., B.S.308; 1943.

84 *Engineering Drawing Practice*, B.S.I., B.S.308: 1953.

85 *Historical Notes on Drawing Instruments*, V & E Manufacturing Co., Pasadena, California, USA, c. 1959.

86 *Mechanical Engineering Drawing Standard, CSA B78.1–1954, and 1959*, Canadian Standards Association.

236

INDEX

INDEX